Livia

PUFFI

THE HALFMEN OF O

Maurice Gee is one of New Zealand's best-known writers, for both adults and children. He has won a number of literary awards, including the Wattie Award, the Deutz Medal for Fiction, and the New Zealand Fiction Award. He has also won the New Zealand Children's Book of the Year Award. In 2003 he received an inaugural New Zealand Icon Award and in 2004 he received a Prime Minister's Award for Literary Achievement.

Maurice Gee's novels include the *Plumb* trilogy, *Going West*, *Prowlers*, *Live Bodies* and *The Scornful Moon*. He has also written a number of children's novels, the most recent being *The Fat Man*, *Orchard Street* and *Hostel Girl*.

Maurice lives in Wellington with his wife Margareta, and has two daughters and a son.

Also by Maurice Gee

The
O
Trilogy

THE HALFMEN OF O

MAURICE GEE

PUFFIN BOOKS

PUFFIN BOOKS
Published by the Penguin Group
Penguin Group (NZ), 67 Apollo Drive, Rosedale,
North Shore 0632, New Zealand (a division of Pearson New Zealand Ltd)
Penguin Group (USA) Inc., 375 Hudson Street,
New York, New York 10014, USA
Penguin Group (Canada), 90 Eglinton Avenue East, Suite 700, Toronto,
Ontario, M4P 2Y3, Canada (a division of Pearson Penguin Canada Inc.)
Penguin Books Ltd, 80 Strand, London, WC2R 0RL, England
Penguin Ireland, 25 St Stephen's Green,
Dublin 2, Ireland (a division of Penguin Books Ltd)
Penguin Group (Australia), 707 Collins Street, Melbourne,
Victoria 3008, Australia (a division of Pearson Australia Group Pty Ltd)
Penguin Books India Pvt Ltd, 11, Community Centre,
Panchsheel Park, New Delhi - 110 017, India
Penguin Books (South Africa) (Pty) Ltd, 24 Sturdee Avenue,
Rosebank, Johannesburg 2196, South Africa
Penguin Books Ltd, Registered Offices: 80 Strand, London, WC2R 0RL, England

First published in 1982 by Oxford University Press
First published in Puffin Books, 1984
This edition published in 2005

Printed and bound in Australia by Griffin Press

ISBN 978 0 14331 834 7
A catalogue record for this book is available
from the National Library of New Zealand.

www.penguin.co.nz

For Abigail

For Abigail

Contents

1

The Message

Our story begins on Lodestone Creek one summer holiday. At least, Nick's part in it starts there. Susan had been involved for the whole of her life, though she did not know it. And Jimmy Jaspers, with his nose for an easy dollar, had been working for the Halfies since he came to the creek in spring. They found him when he started fossicking round the gorge. But he had only glimpsed their world, and though he thought he had the Halfies sized up, and knew they were tough as old boots, he didn't have a glimmer of their real nature. He thought he would be more than a match for them. As Brand was to say, Jimmy did not really understand evil.

But to get back to Lodestone Creek. It ran down out of the bush through the Ferris farm and joined the river at Devil's Elbow. Some early miner had given the place that name. He must have been down on his luck. There was nothing sinister about the bend, and the farm enclosed in it was a lively place – mooing cows, gobbling turkeys, that sort of thing. It lay south of Collingwood in Golden Bay, in one of the lonelier corners of New Zealand.

Susan Ferris had lived there all her life. Nicholas Quinn, her cousin, came with his parents for a couple of weeks each January. He lived in Auckland, far away. Nick and Susan pretended that they got on pretty well. It kept the grown-ups happy. In fact, Susan found Nick's boastfulness hard to take. He seemed to think that people who lived in cities were the only ones who knew anything. Five minutes with him was enough. Then she had to get off on her own. So he accused her of being stuck-up. He thought she was weird as well. He was not alone in that. His mother, Susan's aunt, declared her strange, and his father had been heard to say that she needed a swift kick in the rear-end to wake her up. Nick agreed with that.

This year – the year of our story – she seemed worse. Nick and his mother and father had driven down the length of the North Island. They had crossed the strait on the ferry – rolling in ten-foot waves – and driven through the Rai Valley and Nelson and over the Takaka Hill and through Golden Bay. They reached the farm on the bend of the river and it seemed to Nick they had been weeks on the road. But when he found Susan by the waterfall on Lodestone Creek all she could say was, 'Oh, it's you.' She went on staring into the water.

He was mortified. She didn't have to pretend to like him but she might say hello. A year ago he would have pushed her in. Today he just got in his togs and dived in the pool, straight into whatever it was she was staring at in there. He felt he was making a sharp come-back. But when he came up from his dive she was walking down to the river – strolling away, careless, quite remote, and he realized he hadn't hurt her at all, she hadn't even noticed.

'You keep out of my way and I'll keep out of yours,' he yelled. She made no sign of having heard, but kept on walking neatly over the boulders, her blue towel trailing from her hand, and soon she went out of sight towards the Elbow.

'That got rid of her,' Nick said. But he was disappointed. He'd hoped they might be better friends this year. It was time they stopped carrying on like a couple of kids.

Soon he forgot her. He stood under the waterfall and felt it beat on him like hammers. It seemed to be trying to nail him into the rocks. When he'd had enough of that he climbed to the top of the fall – taking care, making sure of each grip. It was a long way down. But heights didn't scare him. Rock climbing was a sport he meant to take up when he was older. He sunbathed on a warm stone ledge at the top, with water running by so clear that it magnified the pebbles. This stream flowing into the Aorere River was his favourite place in all the world. He saw it for only a couple of weeks each summer, but it was more real to him than the quarter-acre section he lived on in Mt Eden. Sometimes he lay in bed at night and travelled up it in his mind, from the waterfall to the place where the gorge closed in like a pair of grey stone hands making a steeple. This year he meant to try panning for gold. The creek had been worked over pretty thoroughly in the old days, but it was worth a try. Prospectors came there still. It wasn't called Lodestone Creek for nothing.

Nick was one of those people who could not keep still. He spent five minutes lying in the sun and then he was up to have a look at the gorge. One day he meant to go through and see what was on the other side. Susan's father had said to stay out of it; there were deep holes and falls of rock, and, he said, giant eels that would take your foot off with a single bite, but he grinned when he said it and Nick knew he was only having him on. Susan had said there was an old gold mine on the other side. She had been into the shaft a little way, but the timber holding up the roof was rotten and it was dangerous to go far. She seemed to be warning him, but he took it as a challenge. If she could go in it would be easy for him. One day soon he was going to try.

He ran along rocky shelves sloping to the water. It was a game with him to travel up the creek without getting his feet wet. It meant making long jumps, and stepping on boulders that tipped under you, and crawling along stone walls like a fly. He made it easily that day, probably because he was a year older. Soon the noise of the waterfall faded. He stopped. Far away cattle were mooing. It was getting on for milking time. A dog barked. Insects sang. But there was another sound. It was like a motor – like a chain-saw or mower, very distant. Then he noticed that instead of being clear as glass the water had taken on a brown cloudiness. Someone or something up ahead was stirring it up. He went on curiously. The noise became louder; and soon there was no mistaking it: the noise of a two-stroke engine. It came racketing down Lodestone Creek, bouncing off the rock walls, slamming here and there, until Nick thought the top would come off his head. Already he'd guessed what it was: some sort of home-made suction dredge.

He came round the corner and saw it – the motor from a Morrison mower floating on a raft no bigger than the top of a school desk. It made such a hideous noise in the stream bed that everything, the trees, the boulders, seemed to vibrate and be on the point of falling apart. Nick yelled out but could not hear his voice. This wasn't gold prospecting, he thought, this was like being in the middle of Queen Street.

An old man was wading in the stream, bent almost double, sweeping the bottom with a gadget like a vacuum cleaner. He was wearing boots and thick trousers, held up by a knotted piece of twine. He had no shirt but a woollen singlet that might once have been pink. Nick came up on him, jumping along the boulders.

'Gidday,' he yelled. The old man did not hear. Nick came round and looked at him side on. He was an ugly old man: a big rough nose, coloured with veins, a drooping lower lip, all wet with spit and yellow with tobacco, and loose skin under his chin, like a turkey's wattles. Nick didn't mind. He seemed like a real prospector, one of those old blokes with a pack and shovel who'd worked the rivers in the old days.

'You finding any gold?' he yelled.

The old man saw him. He swung round eyes of a reddish colour and pinned Nick on them. Then he ploughed back to his motor and switched it off. A sudden dreadful absence of noise came on Lodestone Creek. It seemed to make Nick dizzy. He couldn't move. The old man came at him, churning up water with his boots.

'You been spyin' on me?' He put out a hand large as a dinner plate, tough and brown as boot-leather, and held Nick by his jaw. 'Let's 'ave a look at yer, sonny.' He forced him up against a boulder. Nick tried to cry out but could make no sound. The old man's fingers dug into his cheeks. Breath fell on his face, heavy and wet. It had the stink of carbide and tobacco.

'Yeah,' growled the old man, 'you got 'er face. How's that, eh? Yer better tell me sonny, else I'll bash yer.'

He's mad, Nick thought. His eyes were watering and he tasted blood in his mouth. He tried to break away. The old man let his face go and gripped him by his arms. His fingers dug in like clamps.

'Fire away, sonny boy.'

'What –?' Nick said. He swallowed. 'What do you want to know?'

'How come you got 'er face?'

'Who?'

'That girl with the yeller hair.'

'Susan? You mean Susan?'

'Dunno 'er name. I seen 'er though. She's the one. Looks like you, she does.'

Nick held his head as far back as he could, trying to get away from that dreadful breath. 'She's my cousin,' he managed to get out.

'Ahh. That's it, eh? Cousins, eh? Listen younker, I'm gunner let yer go, but don't yer try an' run, see? I can move. I can catch yer any day.'

Nick believed him. 'What do you want?' he said, almost crying. Something terrible was happening, but he could not tell what it was. The old man let him go.

'Yer can take 'er a message, see. And don't yer tell anyone. No one but 'er.'

'All right,' Nick said. All he wanted was to get away. The old man gave a growl. He stepped back, keeping his eyes on Nick. 'Stan' still.' He bent down and fished in the water with his hand. In a moment he came up with a flat pebble. He took a clasp knife from his pocket and opened a blade. 'Keep still, sonny. I can chuck this thing.' He began to scratch the pebble.

Nick swallowed. He ran his tongue over the bruised insides of his cheeks. He massaged his arms. The old man gave a grin. 'Didn't mean to hurt yer, younker. Get this message to 'er an' I'll give yer some of me gold.'

'I don't want it,' Nick said.

'Suit yerself. 'Ere now, yer take this. Yer give it ter that girlie. Not when anyone's round, mind. Else I'll come fer yer. I'll do yer in.'

Nick took the pebble. He did not look at it. 'Can I go now?'

'Yer can go. Pansy sort of kid, ain't yer? I reckon that girl's got more fight. Not that it'll do 'er any good. Get goin' before I bash yer.' He raised his arm and made as if to strike Nick's face back-handed.

Nick ducked. He ran. His head was dizzy, almost as if he had been struck. He heard the old man laughing, but did not turn back. Instead of going down the creek he climbed through the scrub into a paddock and started across it to the swing-bridge over the river. His towel and clothes were at the waterfall, but never mind that. All he wanted was to get to the house and tell someone, get the police down to arrest the old man. Tears ran down his face. He felt he had been close to something evil.

As he ran he heard the motor start. It sounded flat and deadly. But at least it meant the old man wasn't after him. He slowed down and became aware of the pebble in his hand. He raised his arm to send it flying, then realized it was evidence, it was proof the old man was mad. He looked at it. The message stood out white on the grey stone. He stared at it without understanding. It was no word but some sort of diagram. He turned it upside-down but it made no more sense that way. It was a rough circle with a curve like an S running through it. Somehow it frightened him. He ran again, threading his way through patches of blackberry. The sound of the motor died away. The sun was sinking over the mountains. The thought of running home through shadows filled Nick with dread. He went between the concrete blocks and steel wires anchoring the swing-bridge. Then he stopped.

Susan was on the bridge. She was leaning on the rail half-way across, with her blue towel draped about her neck, staring in her dreamy way down into the depths, past the granite boulders large as houses, to where the water turned its deepest green.

Nick went on again. The bridge began to bounce. She gave a start and turned to watch him coming. 'Nick,' she said, when he got close. He made no answer, tried to push by her. But she said, 'Nick, I'm sorry. I didn't mean to be rude. It's nice you've come.'

'Yeah,' Nick said.

'Nick –' she looked at him closely, 'what's the matter? How did you hurt your face?'

'Didn't hurt it.'

'You've got bruises.'

He felt his face where the old man had dug his fingers in. He shook his head. 'Some old loony up there.'

'Where? Did he hit you?'

'Lodestone Creek. He reckoned he was giving me a message.'

'What message? Who for?'

'He was off his rocker. He had a knife. I'm going to the police.'

'What message, Nick? Please. Was it for me?'

'Why should it be?' But he was alarmed at the change in her. Under its summer tan her face had gone white as paper. The deep green of the river showed in her eyes.

'Give it to me, Nick.'

Reluctantly he held the pebble out. 'It doesn't make sense. And I want it back. It's evidence.'

She took the pebble, held it lightly in her finger and thumb,

15

like a skimmer. She turned it slowly round, looking at it. A tiny secret smile came on her mouth.

'What was he like? The man who gave it to you?'

'A nut-case,' Nick said. 'And he ponged. He's got away from some loony-bin, I reckon.'

She did not seem to hear. 'Did he have ... No, it doesn't matter.'

'He had bad breath. Give me that. I want it for the police.'

'No, it's mine. He said it was for me.'

'He damn near broke my jaw,' Nick said. 'And he reckoned he'd chuck his knife at me.'

Her face became uncertain. She bit her lower lip. 'He's kind.'

'Have you ever seen him? He reckoned he'd come after me and murder me.'

'No. He must be pretending. Don't tell anyone. Please.'

'You're as mad as he is.'

'I've been waiting for this message all my life. Nick, I've got to see him. Let me have one day. Let me have tomorrow. Then you can tell who you like.'

'I'm not letting you go up there.'

'There's no danger.'

'What does it mean, that message?'

'I don't know.'

He made an angry sound.

'It's true, Nick. I know what it is, but I don't know what it means. Let me find out.'

'How?'

'By talking to him.'

Shadows fell on the bridge. 'Not tonight. I reckon it's dangerous. Tomorrow morning. And I'm coming too.'

'No,' she said. And that had such a sure and heavy sound he could not argue. 'When I come back I'll tell you all about it. Will you promise me, Nick?'

He felt a kind of power coming from her. It was almost as

16

if she was hypnotizing him. She took his hand. He nodded. He felt he was making some dreadful mistake, putting her in danger. 'All right,' he said; and with those words a door in him clanged shut, he could not escape. He understood for the first time how much he liked her. In spite of their squabbling, in spite of all their differences, she was precious to him, as though she were sister more than cousin.

They walked home side by side. Nick changed in his room. He told his mother he'd bruised his jaw when he'd slipped climbing a tree. At the dinner table he watched Susan. She was as silent as ever, but now and then she gave her hidden smile. His aunt made remarks about his city appetite. When he thought of that old man his throat closed up and he could not swallow his food.

They all watched television. Instead of the street lights and the screech of cars Nick was used to, outside was nothing but blackness and silence. He went to the window and looked out. There was a kind of waiting stillness out there, and against it the laughter on the set seemed no more than a chirping of insects. No lights. Black hills. A starry sky. Away south were endless valleys and mountains. Lead Hills. Boulder Lake. Gladiator Peak. West was the Heaphy Track – three days lonely walking to the cliffs and giant waves of the Tasman Sea. He shivered. Out in the dark the waterfall was falling, Lodestone Creek ran silent in its gorge. There, in the bush, a mad old man was sleeping, wrapped in blankets with his carbide stink. Nick made up his mind he had to tell someone. He turned back to the room. Susan was watching him. She gave a small shake of her head. She must know what he was thinking. He frowned at her and felt his aching jaw. Please – she made the silent word with her mouth. And he shrugged, and looked at his mother and father, at his uncle and aunt, laughing, with their faces red, at some joke on the TV set. What could he tell them? What help would they be? He turned back and looked into the night.

At ten o'clock he said good-night to the adults and went to bed. He said he was tired after all that driving. His mother blew him a kiss.

He'd been in bed ten minutes when Susan opened the door and put her head in. 'Good-night, Nick. Thank you.' She was gone. He imagined her lying in her bed, holding that pebble with its crazy 'message', planning what she was going to do. He could not let her. She hadn't seen that man. Nick knew he was evil. He'd felt his hands, and seen his eyes, and smelt the chemical stink of his breath. Susan didn't know what she was getting into. But he'd made her a promise and he knew he couldn't break it. There was only one thing he could do. He could follow her, he could watch without her knowing. That way he'd be able to run for help.

When he'd decided that he felt better. He rolled over. His bed was cool. Soon he went to sleep. But uneasiness followed him even there. Shapes came floating in his dreams, hands came after him, and eyes of hideous red grew up in the dark and peered at him. He heard a screeching sound, and he woke sweating. It was a mosquito buzzing round his face. He gave a sigh, thankful it was nothing worse. But he knew he'd have a hard time getting back to sleep. His arms ached and his jaw was throbbing. He sat up. His mouth was dry as sandpaper. Silently he went down to the kitchen for some water.

In the lounge the adults had turned off the TV set. They were talking – having a nightcap, from the sound of glasses. He wished he could go in and talk to them. He drank his water, listening at the door. They sounded serious. Soon he understood why. They were talking about Susan. 'Doctor,' someone murmured, 'psychiatrist.' 'Not in the real world.' He went closer. Susan's mother: she had a tinny voice, usually sharp with laughter or complaint. Now it seemed to have a grieving edge. 'She was like that when she was a baby. Remember Ted, how she'd be looking away, way out over the horizon, as though there was something there only she could see?'

'Funny birth she had,' Uncle Ted said. 'Something went wrong there. That's what I reckon. Blame it on the flood.'

'It's more than that,' came Aunt Pattie's voice. 'It was that old man. I know it was.'

Nick listened, hardly breathing. His aunt fell into a kind of tearful sing-song. Uncle Ted put a rumbling word in here and there. Twelve years ago. Nick could almost see it. They lived in the old house then, the one they used as a hay barn now. The baby was due. But there was flooding in the valley, Uncle Ted could not get his wife to the hospital. He could not even get his neighbour's help. So, in the little room upstairs, under the sloping roof, while rain hammered on the iron, he delivered the baby himself. Everything went smoothly. At one o'clock she arrived. Susan. A perfect little girl. He wrapped her tightly in blankets and put her in a bassinet by the bed. He made his wife comfortable. Then he left her dozing and went down to the kitchen to make a pot of tea. He was worn out. After a while he went to sleep himself, with his head on the table.

'Then I heard this awful screech.'

He rushed upstairs. Aunt Pattie was sitting up in bed screaming.

'I woke up and saw him,' Aunt Pattie said. 'He was standing by the bassinet. He was leaning over her.'

It was a little old man. He had white hair and a white beard, she saw it plainly in the light of the lamp Ted had left burning. But the strangest thing, the most frightening thing, was the colour of his skin. 'I saw it when I screamed. He looked at me. He was like someone from a flying saucer.' His skin had a reddish colour and seemed to glow from within.

'Now Pattie, now,' Uncle Ted said, 'that was imagination. You'd just gone through a pretty tough time. He was some old prospector. They're always hanging round here, fossicking up the creeks. There's one up there now.'

'It was red. I saw him. I know.'

'Well, well,' Uncle Ted said, 'it might have been a trick of the light. But he was there all right. I got a look at him, just saw him duck out the door when I went to the bed. Might have been old but he sure was quick.'

Uncle Ted chased him down the stairs and out of the house. He did not follow far. The old man vanished like a ghost into the night, into the beating rain.

'I came back to poor old Pattie here. She'd grabbed the baby and was holding it. But I don't reckon he'd meant her any harm. He'd unwrapped her blankets a bit.'

'He put her birthmark on her,' Aunt Pattie said.

'Now, Pattie.'

'He did. She had no mark till he touched her.'

'Well,' Uncle Ted admitted, 'I'd had a pretty good look at her. I didn't see any mark. But when Pattie looked she had this round spot, here, on the inside of her wrist. And a sort of patch up her arm and shoulder.'

'He put it on her. You know that.'

Uncle Ted said nothing. And by the door, in the dark of the kitchen, Nick began to shiver. It was all coming clear. The birthmark. But Uncle Ted was going on with the story. The rains stopped. The floods went down. The doctor got through and had a good look at the baby. She was all right. The birthmark was nothing to worry about. Lots of kids had those. He wouldn't listen to talk about funny old men. Reckoned that was just imagination.

'It wasn't,' Aunt Pattie said.

'No, it wasn't,' said Uncle Ted. 'I went up Lodestone Creek after the flood. Checking stock. I found him up there. Up by the old gold mine. Been dead about three days. He'd fallen down a cliff and broke his neck.'

'Tell them the rest,' Aunt Pattie said.

'Well,' said Uncle Ted. He sounded nervous. 'I had a good look at him, see. He did have a sort of red skin. But that was nothing – just sort of weather-beaten, I reckon. What he did have though was a birthmark. Here, on the inside of his wrist. Same as Susan's. Same place. Same colour.'

'There,' Aunt Pattie said. 'And Susan's been strange ever since.'

'She's a funny kid, all right,' Uncle Ted said.

There was more clinking of glasses. Nobody spoke for a while. Then Nick's parents began making comforting sounds. He could tell they thought Uncle Ted and Aunt Pattie were a bit weird themselves. He could imagine them giving each other secret looks and little winks. But Nick knew better. He turned and went quietly back to his room. He could understand Susan now, and he felt a deep loyalty to her. He understood her need to talk to that old man. He even understood what the message was.

Nick had seen the birthmark on the inside of her wrist. It was about the size of a fifty-cent piece. Patches and smears trailed away from it up her arm. It was almost as if someone had painted a circle, very neatly, and then been given a fright and dragged his brush away. But if you looked more closely you saw the mark on her wrist had two parts. Each was shaped like a tear drop, curved like a moon. They fitted into each other perfectly. One was bright red, almost purple; and the other golden brown. In summer it almost vanished in Susan's tan.

Nick climbed into bed. He pulled the sheet up to his chin. He had it all worked out. If someone wanted to draw a mark like that, and only had a pebble and a knife, he'd scratch a circle on the stone, then through it he'd draw a curved mark like an S.

Nick thought of Susan sleeping in her bed, holding that strange message in her hand.

2

Jimmy Jaspers

It was mid-morning when Susan started out. Nick was in the orchard picking plums. He caught a glimpse of her blue T-shirt as she went down the track leading to the river. He ran to the house and put the plums on the bench.

'I'm going for a swim.'

'Susan's just gone,' Aunt Pattie said. 'You'll catch her if you hurry.'

He grabbed his togs and ran down to the track. Once there, he did not hurry. He kept her in sight as she walked through the scrub and over the swing bridge. She turned aside when she reached the paddock, and Nick saw she meant to go up the creek. That gave him the time he needed. He waited until she was out of sight, then ran up the paddock through the islands of blackberry, taking the way he'd travelled the previous evening. Soon he heard the distant noise of the old man's suction dredge.

When he came to the scrub he went more slowly. The sound of the motor drowned out everything, but he had begun to see the old man as not belonging in the natural world. There was no telling what he might be able to do: hear like a cat? see in the dark with those eyes? He slipped by the tree trunks, through the ferns and mossy boulders, like a shadow. He saw he had made a mistake in wearing bright-coloured clothes.

Lodestone Creek seemed to vibrate in a kind of patient agony under the noise of that hideous engine. The old man was busily sweeping the shallows, but as Nick came to rest in a hidden cleft between two giant boulders, he straightened up and sent his red glare up and down the creek. He had sensed something. Nick shivered. The old man splashed across to the

raft and switched the motor off. Again that menacing silence.
Nick tried not to breathe. But after standing for a moment,
hands on hips, the old man went to the bank and sat down. A
billy was steaming over a fire of twigs. He took a mug from
his pack and poured in tea red as blood. He sucked it through
his lips with a plug-hole noise. Nick watched him, fascinated.
For all his age, there was about him an air of being coiled ready
to spring. It gave him the kind of menace one felt in a wild
boar.

He lifted his mug again, sucked at it noisily, wiped his
mouth with his hand. Suddenly he was still, with the mug
half-way to his mouth. He looked under his eyebrows down
the creek. Nick followed his gaze. There was Susan. She had
come up silently, and now she stood on a dry stone in the creek
and watched the old man with a curious expression, half fright,
half expectation. He put his mug down carefully. He grinned
at her, showing crooked teeth yellow as corn.

'So girlie,' he said, 'that nipper give yer me message?'

Susan stood with her feet wide apart. Nick saw she was
ready to move back the way she had come. The old man saw
it too. He gave a laugh.

'Come and talk to me, girlie. I don't bite.'

'Who are you?' Susan said. Her voice was soft, a whisper.

The old man winked cunningly. He stroked his chin and the
sound of his hand rasping whiskers came clearly over the creek.

'Ah, that'd be tellin'. But I know all about yer. Nothin's
secret from me.' He raised his finger, grinning, and drew a
circle in the air. He made a curving line through it: an S. It
seemed to hypnotize Susan. She moved closer to him, stepping
off the rock and approaching along the shingle at the creek-
side. She stopped again, out of his reach, and he said in a
wheedling tone, 'Yer don't have ter be scared of ole Jimmy
Jaspers.'

'Are you the one who put the mark on me?'

'What mark, girlie? Show me the mark. I gotter be sure.'

23

Susan raised her arm. She showed her wrist. Nick saw the birthmark plainly. It seemed to shine like a brand-new coin.

'Yeah,' the old man said, 'that's the one. Lemme have a squizz. Come a bit closer.'

Don't go, Nick wanted to shout. She seemed to be less cautious now. She stepped up to the old man, still showing her wrist, and he nodded and looked at her sidelong. 'I reckon that's it, all rightie. No mistake. Ha! Tough luck, girl.' His hand shot out. He had her by the wrist. She struggled but he gave a laugh. 'Don't wriggle. Yer can't get away. Ole Jimmy's got yer.'

'Stop, you're hurting me.'

'Don't make no difference.' But he relaxed his grip. 'Sit down. Keep still. 'Tain't me yer gotter be scared of.'

'Who are you?'

'Jimmy Jaspers. That's all yer need ter know.'

'You're not the one who put the mark on me.'

'Never said I was.'

'Where is he? I want to see him.'

'Too late fer that. They fixed 'im long ago.'

'What −' Susan's face had a look of such shock and grief Nick felt himself stretching out his hands to comfort her.

'They bust 'is neck. They don't muck about, them Halfies don't.'

'He can't be dead,' Susan cried. 'I've been waiting. I've been waiting all my life.'

'Wasted yer time then, didn' yer?' He snapped his fingers, sharp as cracking bones. 'No trouble ter them geezers. Lemme give yer some advice. Do what they says.'

Tears were running down Susan's face. The old man let go her wrist. He looked down at her, seeming pleased at her sorrow. 'Waterworks won't get yer nowhere. I gotter send yer through.' He stepped over his fire and rummaged in his pack. Now, Nick thought, now was the time for Susan to run. He wanted to shout at her, but she was so crumpled, so white,

24

crouched on the ground, that he knew she'd never make it. He felt helpless. What should he do? Go for help? But then he wouldn't know where the old man took her. He had to keep close and wait for his chance.

The old man came back to Susan. Nick strained to see what he had in his hand. It was something blue, glittering dully. He said roughly, 'Come on, girl. Time yer had a sniff.'

Susan looked up at him. She did not seem to hear properly. She rubbed her wet face with her hands.

'Nuff of that. On yer feet.' He pulled her up by her arm. It shook her out of her grief and she began to struggle. 'Keep still, damn yer. Like a ruddy eel.' He slipped his hand round her back, grabbing a fistful of hair. Susan cried out.

'Stop wrigglin' an' it won't hurt. Now. All yer gotter do is sniff this 'ere.'

Nick saw it clearly: a blue bottle about the size of a miniature whisky bottle. The old man held it in three fingers and worked the cork out with his forefinger and thumb. It came out with a soft pop. He dropped it on the ground. 'Come on. This is better'n French perfoom.'

A yellow smoke began to come from the bottle. It oozed up, almost solid, swaying like a snake. Nick thought it was alive. He smelt again the carbide stink. Susan pulled her head back, threw it back between her shoulder blades, trying to get away from the yellow thing that twisted at her face. But the old man gave her hair a jerk and held her still. The smoke turned easily and coiled by her mouth. Nick saw she was holding her breath. He was holding his own.

Jimmy Jaspers laughed. 'Come on girlie, you'll go pop in a minute.' And in the end she had to draw in breath; and Nick saw the yellow smoke rush in like a live thing through her mouth.

The old man let her drop. He picked up the cork and jammed it in the bottle. A puff of yellow drifted over the creek. It seemed to come at Nick and he shrank down. But it went high over him and broke and vanished in the leaves of the trees. When he looked out again the old man was putting the bottle in his pack. Susan was on her knees, with her head hanging down and her hair trailing on the ground. The old man buckled his pack. He grinned at her.

'Better get goin', girlie. Doesn't pay ter keep them Halfies waitin'.'

Susan raised her head. She did not look at him but seemed to glare over the creek. Her face was tightened in a painful grimace. And her eyes, staring blindly, had changed their colour to a reddish-brown. Nick felt the hair prickle on his neck. She stood up. Jimmy Jaspers watched her with a grin. 'Tell 'em I'll be comin' fer me gold.'

Susan did not make any sign of hearing. She turned and walked stiffly away up Lodestone Creek. She made no attempt to walk on the shingle or move from rock to rock, but marched in a wooden way through the water, not caring as it came up her legs and wet her shorts. Her hair lay in a tangle on her back. She came to a bend in the creek, turned mechanically, and went out of sight.

Jimmy Jaspers watched her. He did a capering dance, squelching on the shingle fan with his water-logged boots. 'Whee,' he yelled, 'I'm gunner be rich.'

Nick waited no longer. He slipped back out of the boulders, scuttled up through the bush and ran along the paddock again. Soon he came to its end and followed a path in the scrub. It wound towards the creek, and plunged at last down the face of a cliff to the water. He saw Susan passing below him, still walking in that stiff unhuman way. 'Susan,' he called softly. She did not seem to hear. 'Susan it's me.' She went on and passed from sight. Nick looked cautiously back down the creek. No sign of Jimmy Jaspers. He scrambled down and jumped into the shallow water. He was faster than Susan, he knew. It would be no trouble catching her.

She was nearly at the gorge when he grabbed her shoulder.

'Susan. Stop, it's me.' She turned her face to him. The burning smell of carbide sent him reeling back. Her red eyes glared at him like fire. She shook herself free and ploughed on through the water. He came at her again. 'Susan, stop. He's drugged you. You've got to listen.' He grabbed her by the waist and wrestled her down in the water. She thrashed with her arms and legs, trying to break away. He held her down. 'Susan, come on. We've got to get you home.' He saw something in her eyes, a flash of blue, flecks of blue, swimming, sinking, underneath the red. That had to be her, that had to be Susan, fighting to get free of the drug.

'Nick,' she said, 'Nick. Oh help me, Nick.' But as she spoke her body kept pulling away, straining to continue that robot walk up Lodestone Creek. And when he lifted her to her feet and dragged her back a few steps towards home, she began to scream; a thin despairing sound like the screaming of a shot rabbit. 'Oh Nick, oh Nick, it's pulling me. Oh, let me go. It's pulling off my head.' He felt the desperate straining in her, saw her eyes straining in her face. He let her go. At once she set up that wooden walking, ploughed ahead and went into the gorge. All he could do was follow. The grey walls closed over them. The water deepened. He thought for a moment of those giant eels, and then stopped thinking. Nothing was important now except staying close to Susan, saving her.

She kept ahead of him, walking up to her waist, then up to her armpits, in the black water. The walls of the gorge hung above, leaning in a way that made Nick dizzy. The sky was a thread of blue. He swam side-stroke after her. At last they came out, and a valley he had never seen opened up before him. Susan waded to the bank and set off again. He walked at her side, bending to see her face. Once he tried to hold her by the shoulder, but she sobbed as if he had struck her. 'Nick, Nick, it's pulling me.' There was no way he could help. He held her hand and kept close by her side.

The valley walls began to close in. Two long mounds,

curiously even, grown over with small trees and weeds, thrust out from the foot of a cliff. Susan climbed one, and Nick, keeping close, saw they were tailings from a mine. Half hidden in ferns was the mouth of a shaft. It was black as night. Susan stumbled down the side of the mound and went towards it.

'No, Susan. You can't go in there.'

He grabbed her, held her still. She screamed again. 'It hurts. It's pulling off my head.'

'No. I'm not letting you.' Whatever Halfies were, they would be in the mine. He tried to pull her back. 'Oh,' she cried. 'O-oh.' Her eyes seemed to be straining out of her face. From somewhere she found strength to push him off. He went staggering back and lost his balance. By the time he had picked himself up she was passing through the barrier of ferns into the mine.

He did not want to go in there. But he knew he had to. He ran, and pushed the ferns aside and went into a wet darkness that smelled of mould and mud and dead water and carbide. Susan's hair and clothes made a pale blur. He stumbled after them. Light died. 'Susan.' The sound was swallowed up. But a faint luminosity came from Susan's skin. He tried to gain on her and in a moment reached her side and grabbed her hand. His feet splashed in water, his shoulders brushed on rotten stone and rotten timber. The only light came from Susan's face and eyes. She was ghostly. She glowed with a red unnatural light. But her hand in his was warm. That was all he recognized of her.

Presently she stopped. She tried to free herself. He would not let her go. He saw they had come to the end of the shaft. Relief overwhelmed him. No Halfies, whatever they were. And nowhere for Susan to go. She would have to come home. He tried to pull her back. But she braced herself and stood firmly. In a voice he did not recognize she said, 'Let go my hand.'

28

'Come home, Susan. We'll get a doctor. We'll get the police.'

Her eyes stared redly at him. No trace of blue in them now. 'I'm going through.' As he watched, the light of her skin began to fade. Her eyes grew dim. The weight of her hand in his grew less, and looking down he saw it was transparent, it was like glass. He saw his own hand through it. Then a force like a great wind hurled him back against the tunnel wall. He felt as if he had been struck with hammers. He could not move, but lay tumbled on the wet floor of the shaft and watched Susan fade, grow colourless, shimmer with white light. She was printed on the blackness like a figure in the negative of a photograph. Then she was gone. There was a wet sound, a greedy sucking, like something being dragged through a muddy hole. He thought he heard a faint cry, like the lost cry of a gull in the night. Nothing then. Only the steady sound of dripping water.

He pulled himself to his feet. He ran, half falling, half on hands and knees, knocking lumps of rotting wood from the tunnel walls. The light of the opening grew. He burst out through the ferns and fell on the ground. Then he scrambled away from the dark entrance, away from the horror that lived in there. 'Susan,' he cried. It was a cry of grief and incomprehension. What had just happened was impossible – yet it had happened. And Susan was gone, turned into something impossible, sucked away through some hole into ... where? where?

He lay on the shingle by the creek, sobbing with disbelief. The water chattered by. A fantail dived about him, chirping in a friendly way. The drumming of cicadas filled the air. He lay there listening. Slowly he came to understand that the world was as it should be. Only Jimmy Jaspers, only whatever it was that lived in the mineshaft, did not belong. What had been done to Susan could not happen in the real world. That meant ... it meant that it was magic of some kind. Of an evil kind. But how was he to tell anyone? How could he explain it to his father, his mother, to Susan's parents, to the police? No one was going to believe him. But Susan had to be saved. Wherever she was, someone had to find her and bring her back. He began to understand what he must do.

Slowly he got to his feet. The fantail fluttered away upstream. Nick looked at the mineshaft. It was black as night. 'Right Susan, don't be scared.' There was a way, and he was going to take it. He started off downstream, running steadily. He came to the gorge and started in, walking first, then swimming as the bottom fell away.

He was half-way through, deep in shadows, swimming silently, when he heard a noise: a shrill ugly whistling, like a fault in a radio set. It echoed in the gorge. A small stone plopped in the water close to his face. He swam in close to the wall of the gorge, until the sky was hidden. He was sharp, alert; he knew at once the sound was Jimmy Jaspers whistling. The old man was heading for the mineshaft, making his way along the top of the gorge. More stones splashed in the water. Jimmy Jaspers cursed. The sound was magnified by the gorge. The old man sounded as if he was at Nick's elbow. Nick held his breath. He lay still as a trout in the water. Slowly the sounds died away. When they were gone, when all that was left was his own breathing, Nick started back the way he had come. He swam without letting his arms or legs break the surface. He came out of the gorge in time to see Jimmy Jaspers, wearing his pack, vanish into the hollow between the tailing mounds. He pulled himself out of the water, ran bent almost double to the nearer mound, climbed it carefully, and peered down.

Jaspers had stopped at the entrance to the shaft. He was struggling out of his pack. It fell with a clank on the ground. Nick winced. The bottle, that blue bottle – it must not break. But Jaspers was crouching, unbuckling the straps. His ragged breathing came to Nick on top of the mound. He pushed his hand in the pack, felt around, and pulled out the bottle. It gleamed dully, and Nick watched fascinated as the old man leered at it, bounced it on his palm.

'Now,' Jimmy Jaspers crowed, 'now yer bloddy Halfies, I'm comin' fer me pay. I sent that girlie through and now I want the gold yer promised me.'

He pulled the cork out of the bottle. At once the solid-seeming oily smoke swayed up like a snake. Jimmy Jaspers stared at it cross-eyed. 'Pretty stuff. Reckon it's pretty stuff. C'mon. Gimme a sniff.' The smoke seemed to respond, turned sinuously at him, and seemed to writhe into his mouth and nose. 'Ah,' said Jimmy Jaspers, 'better'n whisky.' He corked the bottle and put it in his pack. Nick could see no change in him. He must be used to it. As for himself, he caught that same carbide smell and tried to keep his breathing shallow.

Jimmy Jaspers straightened up. He was grinning eagerly. 'Stop yer pullin',' he said, 'I don't need no pullin'.' He left his pack lying on the ground and went to the shaft. He pushed the ferns aside, and with a last furtive glare at the valley, passed inside. For a moment the sound of his boots came out but soon it died to a shuffle, then was gone.

Nick crept over the mound. He went cautiously to the pack and saw the bottle gleaming in its depths. He looked at the mine nervously, then took the bottle out. It was very cold. He put his thumb on the cork, making sure it was tight. He did not want that smoke coming out until he was ready.

He went to the mouth of the mine. No sound in there. He listened carefully. Once he thought he heard laughter. The carbide smell was strong. He waited. At last he heard the sound he'd been waiting for: that hideous, greedy sucking-sound, as Jimmy Jaspers passed like dirty water through to wherever it was he was travelling. And wherever that was, Susan was there too. And the Halfies. He shivered. For a moment he had the hideous vision of men split down the middle, from the top right through to the bottom, falling in halves like two planks of timber. Then he shook himself. Susan was there. That was all he really had to worry about. He was the only one who could bring her back.

The ferns tickled his face. He touched them with his fingertips. It was like saying goodbye. He was almost crying with fear, but another part of him was cold and brave. He held up the blue bottle. Something moved in it, coiling lazily. 'Here goes,' Nick said. He pulled out the cork.

The yellow smoke reared out and turned towards him.

3

Odo Cling

It was like being sucked into a dream of red lights streaming in water; then of going deeper, until the light was water, all colour gone, until water was mud, jet black, and mud had turned to earth and earth to stone, and stone was everything, stone was the world and life, stone was air, stone was past and future, stone was the screaming sound she tried to make. And then – before that last tiny consciousness faded away (and she held on to it desperately, for it was all she had) – the whole process went into reverse, there was a painful climbing back, through stone, through earth, through mud, through light and water. It was like being born. It was terrible, and glorious, coming back to life. Red lights streamed again, spinning like whirlpools. The sucking was reversed. She was being thrust up, she was spinning up the walls of a giant funnel into the world after being sucked hungrily into the stomach of death. She screamed with relief.

A bumping of knees, a painful scraping of palms: and she was Susan Ferris, kneeling in cold water in the dark of the mineshaft. Her hair was tangled in a skein round her throat, as though it had been beaten in a storm. She stood up and peeled it away. She drew in a shuddering breath. Nick was gone. There was all about a feeling of such emptiness that she knew no other living thing was close. She was not afraid. A blackness thick as wool was crammed in her eyes. But she had come through something worse than that.

She put out her hands and felt the walls of the tunnel. They were hard and slimy. She felt all about, trying to find which way led to the open. Soon she found it, and set off down the tunnel, feeling her way. It seemed to go on and on. It went round curves she could not remember. But that, she thought, must have been because she had been drugged. She had been sick with the terrible smoke Jimmy Jaspers had thrust under her nose. Her head was clear now and her fingers tingled with life as she felt her way down the midnight walls.

Soon a faint lessening of the darkness showed ahead. She went eagerly towards it. A greyness in it made her pause a moment. It looked as if night were falling out there. She wondered how long she had been in the shaft. Perhaps that hideous dream had lasted the whole of the day. But in that case, where was Nick? Why hadn't he come with help for her?

She hurried on. The grey light grew. It was the colour of lead. She wondered if some dreadful accident had taken place outside. Perhaps the bush had caught fire and smoke had blotted out the sun.

The mouth of the shaft seemed wider than it had been. It was reinforced with logs like railway sleepers. There were no ferns. Susan walked out on a tongue of stone. She looked about, gave a cry, and fell down on her knees.

The creek was gone, the bush was gone, the tailing mounds were gone. And everything was grey: a huge grey cloudless sky, grey land, grey hills rolling endlessly down until they were lost in a haze, ashy stunted trees, twisted unnaturally, grass the colour of tin. But worst of all, most hideous of all, burning without colour overhead, a huge black sun, set up there like an iron hot-plate in the sky.

Susan screamed. She looked at herself. Her skin was grey, her nails gleamed like chips of polished stone. She grabbed a handful of hair and pulled it round. It was grey and dead as an old woman's hair. She cried out with horror and disbelief. She pushed her hands away from her, throwing them away. They were not part of her. Her hair was no part. She refused them. And this grey world in front of her was an evil dream.

34

But it would not go away. She closed her eyes, opened them. Trees, hills, sky, sun – still there. Hands still there, grey as leprosy. She wept grey tears on them.

After a while she climbed to her feet. She turned about. She did not know where to go or what to do. The mouth of the shaft was a black half–circle. She was not going in there, even though going back – trying to find a way through that spinning dream – was the only escape that occurred to her. On either side of the shaft stone walls curved away. Beyond were hills, stretching along the horizon, and mountains with grey snow on them, standing steep and tall, like a file of monks in shapeless habits. Where was she? *Where* was she? This was not her world. This must be hell.

She put her face in her hands. She heard with a kind of wonder the choking sounds that came from her throat. She felt the warmth of tears flowing on her palms. They were the only things that still seemed right.

A voice spoke close to her with a scratchy softness. 'Good! Good! Hee! Your pain is most amusing.'

Susan screamed. The man in front of her had come like a ghost. She stared at him without any understanding. He was no taller than her, and a good deal thinner. He was dressed all in leather and black iron, like a Roman soldier. An iron cap was close about his skull. He was grey, like her; except his eyes. They were red. She was almost glad to see this sign of colour, even though his eyes were bright and cruel.

'Who,' she managed to say, 'who are you?'

'I am Odo Cling.' His voice had the sound of a nail scratching tin. 'I am a Great One. I am Executive Officer. I am Doer of Deeds for the One Who Rules, Otis Claw, Darksoul, Ruler of O, where pain is truth. I am Second. One day I shall rule.' His eyes grew a deeper red. 'I shall bring you to the Pit. I shall be the one. Otis Claw shall make room for me.' He drew himself up taller. He showed his teeth.

Susan stared at him. She was afraid; yet the only thought

she could find was, what a stupid little man! At last she laughed. She could not think of anything else to do.

Odo Cling gave a screech. He struck at her with a short leather whip he held in his hand. She stepped back and it whistled by her face. She turned to run. But it was Odo Cling's turn to laugh. He rattled with mirth.

'Where are you running to, Mixie? Have you not seen?'

By that time Susan had. She came to a halt. All about the tongue of stone silent men were standing. They had come without a sound. They were dressed in black robes, like monks, and had black hoods on their heads. Only their grey hands and leathery feet showed any human resemblance. Deep in their hoods, pinkish eyes watched without expression.

'These are my guards, the Deathguard,' Odo Cling said. 'They move like night and death. You cannot escape. Do not try.' He snapped his fingers. 'Bring her close to me.'

The hooded circle closed on Susan. It drew in like a tightening noose. She turned, looking for a gap, but there was none. Two guards darted out. They had her by her arms before she knew it. She felt their fingers bite upon her elbows. They brought her close to Odo Cling. She saw his burning eyes, and smelt from him the bitter chemical stink of the yellow smoke. He raised his whip and grinned at her. Then he lowered it. 'No. No. I shall deliver her unscarred. Later we shall kill her. The Mark. Let me see it.'

One of the guards seized her arm in both his hands. He thrust it forward for Odo Cling to see. The mark on her wrist showed plainly, one half black, the other a pale grey, only a little darker than the skin surrounding it. Odo Cling bent close. He smiled with a twist of his mouth, and poked his skinny finger at it, but stopped short. Susan saw he was frightened. He beckoned with his whip and a guard stepped from the circle and came to his side.

'Touch it.'

'Lord?'

36

'Touch. Do you disobey me?'

'No, Lord.' The man glided up to Susan. She looked into the dark of his hood and saw his pink eyes swimming with terror. He put his hand out and brought a trembling finger down towards her wrist. But he could not make himself touch. 'Lord?'

Odo Cling flicked his whip across the man's face. 'I shall give you to the dogs.'

'No Lord, I shall touch.' He pushed his finger down. It came to rest on the black half of the mark. Susan felt only the scratch of his fingernail. But he began to tremble. Tears of satisfaction stood in his eyes. 'Lord, there is the glory of all darkness here.'

'Enough,' Odo Cling said. 'The other one.'

'I wish for more.'

Odo Cling slashed his whip down on the man's forearm. 'Enough, I say.' The man cried out. He nursed his arm. 'Forgive me, Lord. The pleasure was too great.'

'The other one.'

'I obey.' He brought his finger down on the pale side of the mark. At once he began to writhe. He raised his face and howled. He tried to pull his hand away but his finger seemed stuck to Susan's skin. 'Lord, the good is here. Save me.'

Odo Cling nodded. Another guard sprang forward and knocked the man away. He lay on the ground sobbing. Odo Cling watched him thoughtfully. He turned to Susan. 'It seems you bear the true Mark. Now, the final test. You.' He jerked his whip at the guard who had sprung forward. 'See what happens when you touch them both.'

This man was better trained. 'Yes, Lord.' He came up to Susan. His pink eyes shone with fear, but he put his hand out steadily and brought his finger down on the black half of the mark. His body shook. He bared his teeth, and brought his thumb down on the other half.

Susan felt nothing. Her arm seemed to be numb. But the instant the man's thumb came to rest a crack like the sound of a stock-whip split the air and the man was lifted and hurled backwards. He turned like a great grey bird, and came down on his back in a tangle of robes. No one moved to help him. He groaned, shook his head and hauled himself into a sitting position. One of his hands dangled useless. With the other he pulled out a pad of cloth on a string at his throat and held it to his nose. In a moment he staggered to his feet. Groaning, he said, 'Lord, it struck like a hammer.'

Another man came forward and looked at him. 'His hand is shattered, Lord.'

Odo Cling turned to Susan. 'Bind her.'

The men holding her drew her arms behind her back and tied them tightly. Odo Cling inspected the knot. 'You are dangerous, Mixie. You are the last enemy.'

'I don't know what you mean,' Susan said. 'I just want to go home.'

'Home?' Odo Cling laughed. 'Soon you will be saying *mother* and *father*. These words have no meaning. You are in O, the world of Halfmen. We shall take you to Darksoul, to the Pit. Then you will die.'

'Lord.' One of the guards came gliding forward. 'Someone approaches in the tunnel.'

Odo Cling listened. He showed his teeth in a grin. 'I thought he would not be long.' Susan, too, guessed who it was whistling that cheerful tune as he stumped along in the dark.

Cling waved his whip. 'Prepare. We must welcome our friend.'

Two of the guards flattened themselves against the rock, one on each side of the tunnel. The rest moved off a little way, dragging Susan with them. They stood in a group, with Odo Cling at their head.

The whistling became louder. It was some gold-town shanty, Susan thought. She wanted to cry a warning, but even more she wanted to see someone from her world. Jimmy Jaspers, when he came stumping into the grey light, was the first thing that had made any sense since she had come out of the tunnel. He saw her, saw the waiting party, gave a grin.

'Ah, you got 'er? I done all right, Mr Cling. Now I've come fer me gold.'

Odo Cling smiled. 'Welcome again to O, Jimmy Jaspers. You shall have your reward.'

'Where is it, then? A sack o' gold, yer said.' He came down the sloping rock to them, and at his back the two Deathguards glided silently.

'The smoke? The bottle? You have brought me that?' Odo Cling said.

'Durn it, no, I fergot,' Jimmy Jaspers said. 'I'll chuck it away when I get back.'

Odo Cling grinned. 'No matter. When some fool finds it and opens it the smoke will escape and that will be that. The tunnel will be closed. Until of course we take our armies through to conquer your world.'

''Ere,' Jimmy Jaspers said, 'yer never told me nothin' about that.'

'There are many things I did not tell you.'

'Yer don't own this world yet from what I can see.'

'No. But soon we will.' Cling flicked his whip at Susan. 'She was the last danger. Now we have her. Thanks to you, Jimmy Jaspers. You have been an excellent servant.'

'You Halfies is a tricky lot. Gimme me gold. I'm gettin' back.'

'So you can warn them? Ah no, Jimmy Jaspers.'

The two guards slid in closer. Susan could stand it no longer. 'Look out,' she screamed. 'Behind you.'

Jaspers lumbered round, but he was too slow. The guards moved like shadows, seized his arms, forced him on his knees.

'Eh, eh,' he cried, 'what's this? I kept me word. I done me part.'

'And now I have no more use for you,' Odo Cling smiled.

'Yer promised me. Yer said yer'd give me gold.'

'I shall give you something better. Death.'

'Yer bloddy twister. I'll get yer fer this.'

'Ha! Amusing. I like you, Jimmy Jaspers. But you are a Mixie. All Mixies die. It is the law. I shall have them kill you quickly though. That is your reward.'

'Yer can't do this. Yer' a bloddy ratbag.'

'Take him,' Odo Cling said.

The guards jerked Jaspers to his feet and dragged him back to the tunnel entrance.

'No, no,' Susan cried. She struggled to get free.

''Elp me, girl. I'm sorry fer what I done.'

'I can't help,' Susan cried. She fought and twisted, but could not escape.

The guards hauled Jimmy Jaspers into the dark. Odo Cling made a sign. A third guard ran up to the tunnel mouth, drawing a long knife from his robes. He went inside. Susan turned away. She began to cry. Her hands were tied at her back and she could not wipe her face.

Bellows of rage came out of the tunnel as Jimmy Jaspers fought. But in a moment they were cut off in a yelp of pain. Something heavy fell on the rock floor. Susan turned around. The three guards came out, one of them wiping his knife on his robes.

'So end all Mixies,' Odo Cling said.

'You promised him gold. And you killed him,' Susan sobbed.

'Promises to Mixed men do not exist. But he betrayed you, yet you cry for him. Most amusing.'

'Does killing people amuse you?'

'Yes. Yes indeed. It is the best thing. Pain and death. But enough. We have a long way to go. Darksoul waits. Bring her.' He started off down a track leading from the platform by the tunnel.

Susan threw a last desperate look behind her, then was pushed roughly along by the guard at her back. She stepped down to the track and went zig-zagging through shale and stunted trees. The black sun was low in the sky. Far below, a river wound towards the fringe of a forest. She guessed Odo Cling was heading for some camp down there and hoped to reach it before night fell.

When the path levelled out she threw a glance behind her but the tunnel was hidden by the brow of the hill. The file of guards coming down made a black zed on the slope. They were, she thought, like a band of Inquisition monks going to watch someone burned at the stake. She trotted desperately after Odo Cling. He was the worst of them, but at least he had said he meant to keep her unharmed for the time being. They crossed a narrow plateau and before starting down the slope beyond it she turned and saw the tunnel in view again. It had shrunk to an insignificant mark on the face of the cliff. She wondered how she would ever find it again if she escaped. Then she almost gave a cry. Something moved up there. It fluttered like a bird in the tunnel mouth. She could not see, she could not quite make out ... Then the guard behind gave a hiss and sent her reeling with a thrust of his palm. They went in file down a new slope, and the tunnel was lost. She knew she would not see it again. But something had moved. She did not even know if it was human. As they went down the shaly slopes, across the plateaux, through a landscape without variation or colour, she clung to that movement as her only hope.

They walked for an hour or more. She saw she had been wrong about reaching a camp. The black sun slid down into the haze beyond the forest and still they seemed no closer to the river than when they had started. Blackness began to grow like a fog in the air. They came down a steep hill, turning among thorny trees, and at the bottom Odo Cling held up his hand.

'Here.'

It was no camp, simply a place to stop. Coarse grass grew

41

among the stones. Odo Cling sat down. He pointed. A guard forced Susan down.

'Give her water.'

She was feeling dizzy and breathless and wanted time to recover, but someone thrust the neck of a flask in her mouth and she drank lukewarm water tasting of mothballs. Odo Cling was eating from a jar brought by one of his men.

'Feed her.'

'No,' Susan said, 'I'm not hungry.'

'You will eat. We have five days to march. I do not want you dying.'

A hand thrust something grey at her mouth. 'No.' She twisted her head away. At once another guard sprang forward. He seized her jaw, forced her mouth open. The first man pushed something slimy inside. Then her mouth was forced shut. Fingers clamped her nose. She had to swallow. It felt horrible – slimy, thick, cold – but the worst part was that it had no taste. It was like swallowing pieces of greasy plastic. They fed her half a dozen, then Odo Cling said, 'Enough.'

She gasped and gagged for a while but the food stayed down.

'Now you will sleep.'

'I want to wash,' she managed to say.

'Tomorrow. When we reach the river.' He signed to one of his men, who took a blanket out of his pack and spread it on the ground.

'Lie on it,' Cling said.

Susan obeyed. The man folded the blanket over her. She shivered. The spiky grass and stones hurt her sides.

'I can't sleep with my hands tied.'

'Do you think we mean to let you escape Mixie?'

'It hurts.'

'Quiet. Another word and I will have you whipped.'

All around the men of the Deathguard were arranging themselves for sleep. They curled up like cats in their black

42

robes. Two men walked silently round the rim of the camp. Two more stood at her head and feet. A night black as coal came down. Later there was a faint lightening as a moon rose behind shifting clouds. She glimpsed it from time to time and it was coloured like pewter and had markings her moon did not have. She slept a little, and woke whimpering. A guard hissed at her. Suddenly Odo Cling's face was bending over her. 'I told you to sleep.'

'I can't. I'm cold. I'm aching all over.'

Cling made an angry sound. He fumbled at his neck. All the guards kept a little bag of something there, and sniffed at it from time to time. Cling, too, had a bag. She had seen him put it to his nose several times on the walk down from the tunnel. Now he thrust it at her face.

'No. No.'

'Sniff. Then you will sleep.'

'No.'

He seized her hair. She cried out with pain. But the hard little bag came down under her nose and over her mouth and a carbide reek filled her and she felt herself hurled into sleep as though by a great blow on her head. For the rest of the night she dreamed hideous dreams that had no shape, that were all twisting and whirling and falling into black pits with no bottom. When she woke in the morning her face was salty with tears. She knew she could not go through another five days of this.

They fed her again and then Odo Cling had her hands untied and let her wash at a small spring in the side of the hill. Guards stood at her back with knives drawn. When they came to tie her again she said, 'Please, tie my hands in front. I won't try to escape.'

'No.'

'I'll walk faster.'

Odo Cling thought. 'No tricks, Mixie.' He signalled the guards. 'Tie them in front.' They bound her tight, eyeing the mark on her wrist. Cling seemed in a good mood. 'Here.' He walked to the edge of the slope and looked out over the falling land. A guard brought Susan to his side. 'See,' Cling pointed, 'tonight we will reach the forest. Then three days to Sheercliff. Then down out of this stinking air into the glory of Darkland. There you will meet Otis Claw.' He grinned. 'I do not know what he plans for you Mixie, but I shall be there to enjoy it all.'

Susan shivered. She tried to concentrate on the view in front. Although much of it was still in shadow, things stood out with a clarity they had lacked the night before. The forest was tar-black. It ran on and on like a huge rumpled blanket on the land. The river curved into it and vanished. She could not see the place Cling had called Sheercliff, but guessed it would be a drop in the land. The forest stopped over there and gave way to a grey murkiness, like an oily pond, spreading out on the horizon. Sunlight gleamed on it. She guessed it was a kind of smog. Underneath lay the place Odo Cling called Darkland. What was that? And who was Otis Claw? She shivered again and looked behind her. The guards were drawn up in a file, ready to move out. Beyond them the land climbed into the sky. Huge grey hills filled the horizon. Here and there the peaks of mountains rose. A dark glow showed where the sun would rise over them. The mountains ran north-east, so Darkland and Sheercliff were off to the west.

She turned to Odo Cling. 'I don't know where I am or why I'm here.'

'You don't need to know.'

'I've got a right. You've taken me away from home.'

'There is no home. And Mixies have no rights. Halfmen rule O. That is enough.'

'I don't know any O. I don't belong here. I'm from Earth.'

Odo Cling sneered. 'Look at your wrist. You belong.'

'What is it? This mark?'

44

'The less you know the less dangerous you are. Enough talk. March. We have a long way to go.'

They started off again. Susan was third in line, behind Cling and one of the guards. She walked more easily with her hands tied in front. She began to wonder if she could dart off to one side and escape among the boulders beside the track. But the guard behind was never more than a step away. He hissed each time she turned to look at him. By midday she was exhausted. They stopped to eat and she sprawled on the ground. When a guard brought her a jar of the grey meat she ate it almost hungrily. She knew she must keep her strength up.

In the early afternoon the track was easier. It ran over a plain where the only obstacle was an occasional outcrop of rock. Susan kept up easily. She began to feel strong and made up her mind that next time she saw a chance she would try to get away. Then, if she could find a sharp stone and cut the rope round her wrists, she should have a good chance of finding her way back to the tunnel – and maybe whatever it was she had seen moving around up there would help her find her way back through the spinning dream to her own world.

They came to the edge of the plain. A long slope fell away to the river and forest. It was broken country, full of ravines and gorges and clumps of trees, and boulders sharp as knives that pointed every way. She felt elated. Surely her chance would come in there. They started down. The path dropped sharply, curving round boulders and cutting across cliff-faces. They went by tumbling streams and waterfalls. Then Susan thought she saw a perfect place. On the left the ground sloped down from the path, then dropped out of sight into a black ravine; but on the right a cleft showed in the cliff. It was full of trees and boulders, closely packed, just right for someone her size to scramble through. If she could get in there she would leave these men in their flapping robes far behind. She grinned with determination.

Odo Cling passed the cleft without a glance. The guard went past. Then Susan came to it. There was a tree bending low to the path and as she came level she took two quick steps, jumped on the trunk, ran along it like a path, and began to haul herself over the boulders. As soon as she was clear of them she would be in the cleft, and climbing, and none of the guards would get near her. There was a slapping of feet on stone, a scrambling sound of hands, a clink of knives. She heard Odo Cling screeching commands. And then it was she saw she had misjudged. The final boulder was too steep for her. She felt for hand-holds desperately, but the surface was smooth. She looked about for ways to go. There was no time. The first guard had her. She spun around, saw his eyes burning, smelt his carbide breath, and saw his knife. She gave a scream. But he did not mean to kill her, only to hold her. His free hand came down on her wrist. He was too eager. He had forgotten. He grasped her by the wrist that had the mark.

At once a flat explosion rattled the air. Susan felt nothing. But the guard gave a shriek as the force in her picked him up and hurled him end over end like a stick, down from the boulders, over the track, on to the sloping ground. He came down like a huge black legless bird, tumbled helplessly in a spray of shingle, and vanished with a shriek into the ravine. A cry came floating up. Then there was nothing.

Susan turned again and tried to run. But in her pause a guard had scrambled up another way and stood above her. Two others came sliding along the rocks. Before she had taken half a dozen steps knives were pricking at her breast and throat. She stopped and stayed absolutely still. She saw their red eyes bulging. These men were aching to kill her.

Odo Cling stood on the path. 'Tie her. Hands behind.' And when that was done, 'Bring her.' They tumbled her down from the boulders. She fell on her knees at Odo Cling's feet.

'So Mixie, you have killed one of my men. I shall make you suffer.'

'I didn't mean to kill him.'

'I should throw you down to join him. I should throw you to the jackals.'

'I don't care what you do.'

'You will care.' He flicked his whip at her cheek. She felt it burn like fire. He laughed. 'That is just a taste. And now we will see how you like travelling in a throttle.' He jerked with the whip and a guard brought a leather collar from his pack. It had ropes running through it. He placed it over Susan's head and pulled it tight on her throat. A guard in front took one rope and a guard behind the other. 'On your feet, Mixie. Any tricks and either one of them can throttle you.'

So they walked through the afternoon. They went through gorges, down the sides of cliffs on paths that would have troubled a goat, tracked across shingle slides, walked on slimy stone beside black streams, and all the time Susan felt that wicked collar pressing on her windpipe. She took care with every step. One slip and the guards would choke her.

The sun was going down when they reached the river. They crossed by a ford and made camp on the edge of the forest. The trees were close-packed and the dark in there was more intense than any Susan had ever seen. She wondered if tomorrow they would travel in the forest. But she had no strength left to be frightened. She drank when a flask was thrust into her mouth and ate more lumps of slimy meat. Then she lay down and tried to sleep. She knew better than to ask Odo Cling to have her hands untied or have the collar taken from her neck. The guards at her head and feet had the ropes tied round their waists. Every time she swallowed she felt the leather pressing on her throat. She tried not to move, tried to breathe softly. Whatever happened, she did not want Odo Cling pressing his horrible sniffing-bag under her nose.

She managed to doze for a while, and woke when the guards were changing. She lay still as everything settled down. Now

47

and then distant animal cries came from the forest. Once a bird like a morepork sounded close. Tears ran down her face. She would never hear real moreporks again, or see fantails, or see her mother and father, or her dopey cousin, Nicholas Quinn. She tried to wipe her face on her blanket. The guard at her head gave his rope a jerk. Then he leaned down and loosened the collar so she could breathe. After a while she dozed again.

She woke with the moon on her face. Grey light filled the campsite. Boulders gleamed in the grass and the trunks of the trees in the forest stood out like an army of soldiers. Something had woken her. Cautiously she turned her head and looked about. The men wrapped in their robes slept without moving. Odo Cling lay only an arm's length away. His breath sang horribly in his nose. Watchmen paced by the forest and river. The guards at her head and feet stood still as stone. Everything was normal. Yet something was wrong. She felt it. Or perhaps something was right. She felt a thrill in her blood at the thought. Then the answer came – a birdcall from the forest.

'Morepork.' A long pause. 'Morepork.'

She felt herself almost choking with delight and anguish. There was no mistake: a morepork, a bird from her world. But somehow she knew it was more than that – she knew it was a message for her alone. Someone from her world was out in the bush, making that call. Someone was coming to rescue her.

She lay still as a cat. Half an hour passed. The watchmen paced. The guards breathed and sighed, exchanged a grunt. Everything was still. Then the moon went behind a cloud. Nothing changed. Rustlings came as men turned in their sleep. The moon slid out again. And something *had* changed. She saw it at once. The watchman by the river, the watchman by the forest, were not there. And all about, motionless and low upon the grass were boulders in the shapes of crouching men. Her guards had not seen. Knowing she was roped, they stood and dozed, hands upon their waists.

Susan held her breath. She felt if she made the smallest movement Odo Cling would wake, the guards would spring into action. She kept her eyes on the boulders. None of them moved. Yet she knew they were men, and knew that they had come to rescue her. She turned her eyes to see the moon. A cloud thick as oil, heavy as an elephant, moved ponderously down on it. A minute more, then the night would turn black as soot, her rescuers would come.

Moving slow as treacle, the cloud blotted out the moon. Again a darkness heavy as wool came on Susan's eyes. She strained to hear, but the stirrings, the faint rustlings, seemed no more than normal night-time noises. When she had almost given up hope, the guard at her head gave a small grunt of surprise. Then he sighed. The man at her feet made a quick movement – she heard the oily scrape of a knife half-drawn from its scabbard – then he sighed too. Straining her ears, she heard mouse-like movements, whisperings of cloth. A voice breathed in the hair about her face, making it stir. 'Be still ... You are safe.' She felt hands at her throat, loosening the collar, lifting it off.

'Thank –'

'Shsh.'

A knife worked on the rope binding her wrists. In a moment she was free. She tried to sit up.

'No,' the voice breathed. 'Stay here. We will come.'

Something crept away. Then she heard faint noises among the sleeping guards. She wondered if her rescuers were moving among them, killing them perhaps. The thought made her feel sick. But in a moment the moon rolled out from behind its cloud and she saw half a dozen small figures, no taller than children, darting among the guards, pressing something to the face of each. Something, she guessed, that knocked them out the way Odo Cling's bag had knocked her out.

She strained her eyes to see who the newcomers were. But the light was too dull. All she could see was that they wore robes of a lighter colour than the Deathguards. They moved as neatly as fish darting in a pond. In a moment their job was done. All the guards were lying stiff and helpless as bales of hay. They laughed, the first normal sound Susan had heard, and started back towards her, pushing the hoods back from their faces.

'Well, Susan Ferris, you are safe. Now we must get away from here.'

She stood up. Her knees creaked. She felt like laughing. But as she tottered, one of her rescuers made a sudden dart. He gave a cry, 'Look out.' She saw a black movement at her side and felt an arm strong as fencing wire lock on her throat. Odo Cling's voice screeched at her ear, like a saw grating on a nail.

'Back! Back, you vermin of the woods.' She saw the gleam of a knife, felt it pricking at the base of her throat. 'Back, I say.'

Her rescuers had halted. They stood in a knot, helplessly. Odo Cling laughed. 'Did you think you could defeat Odo Cling, the Executive Officer? One move and the Mixie dies. I say it, Odo Cling, Doer of Deeds.' He screeched again, more a scream of triumph than a laugh. 'Did you think you had knocked me out with your stink-pads? I am immune. I have taken the cure. No stink-pad works against the great Odo Cling. I lay quiet till I saw my chance. And now I have her. I have the Mixie. And you will stay where you are till my men wake up. Then we will have some sport.'

One of the rescuers shook his head. He seemed dazed, he seemed to have shrunk. 'I'm sorry, Susan.'

'How do you know my name?'

'Quiet!' Odo Cling screamed. His arm tightened round her throat. She managed to smile. She was calm, not the least bit frightened. She knew exactly what she was going to do.

50

'Don't take any notice of Odo Cling. He's not very clever. He's forgotten the most important thing.'

'Quiet, Mixie. I shall cut your tongue out.'

'This,' Susan said. Almost lazily she raised her arm and laid the mark on her wrist on Odo Cling's hand. The detonation so close to her ears made her head seem to split in two. Odo Cling was torn from her so roughly that she staggered and almost fell. But she saw him go spinning high in the air, thin legs poking at angles, and saw him crash down in a tangle over the bodies of his sleeping guards. He lay still.

'That's what he forgot,' Susan said. Then she sat down. She felt rather faint suddenly.

A figure came running from the forest. He wore a robe like the ones her rescuers wore. But his hood was back, she saw his face. He ran through the Deathguards and jumped over Odo Cling. Susan stood up. She took a step towards him. He grabbed her in his arms and hugged her until she could hardly breathe.

'Susan. You're all right. Thank God.'

She started to cry. It was good just to be able to cry. She let her tears run on to his shoulder. 'Nick. Oh, Nick. Where on earth did you come from?'

4

The Woodlanders

The Woodlanders – for so they called themselves – darted among the Deathguards, unbuckling their knives, cutting loose the stink-pads from their necks. They took them in armfuls down to the river and hurled them in.

'Without their weapons and pads they will not dare follow us in the forest,' Brand said. He was leader: a small creature, wiry and tough, with a woolly face and merry eyes. 'But Odo Cling has another camp half a day's march down the river. They will get more weapons there. Then they will be after us. So we must be off. The Deathguards follow scent like dogs. If we have time we will lay false trails for them.'

Susan was standing with her hand in Nick's. She looked about at the black guards and shivered. One or two were starting to moan and stir. 'Is Odo Cling alive?'

'He breathes. Worse luck,' Brand said.

'Can I borrow your knife?' She took Brand's knife and cut the thong securing Cling's whip to his wrist. She threw it into the dark. 'I'm glad he's not dead. I killed a man today.'

'We saw. We have been close.'

'Don't be upset, Sue,' Nick said. 'It was an accident.'

'Yes.'

'But what did you do to him? And Cling?'

'I don't know. My wrist . . .' She looked at it.

'Time for that later,' Brand said. 'They are starting to wake.' He got his men together – but were they men? Although they were small their shape was right. But their hands, even their faces, were covered with fur. She looked at them more closely. Three seemed lighter, quicker. Perhaps they were female. They started off up the edge of the forest and over a low hill, leaving the groaning guards in their empty camp, with Cling stunned in the midst of them.

'He will not give up,' Brand said. 'He will come like a Bloodcat when he is armed. We must get deep in the woods. Can you run, Susan?'

'I'm not sure.'

'Here.' He put his hand in a bag belted to his hip and pulled something out. 'Eat this.'

'What is it?'

'A sort of fern root, Sue,' Nick said. 'They dry it. It tastes like bananas, only better.'

'It will give you strength,' Brand said.

Susan ate. The food felt pleasant in her mouth, it felt like dates, but she was disappointed to find it had no more taste than Odo Cling's meat. She said nothing. It would have seemed ungrateful to have complained. 'Nice, thank you. I'm cold.'

At once a man stepped forward, drew off his robe, and pulled it down over Susan's head. She was warm instantly. She smiled at him standing there in his short grey tunic. 'I can't take your clothes.'

'He is proud to help the wearer of the Mark,' Brand said. 'Now let us run. Odo Cling is awake. You did not throw his whip far enough, Susan. He punishes his men.'

They heard a bloody howling, like cats fighting in the night.

'Yes. Yes. Let's run.'

They went in single file, Brand first, then Nick and Susan. The others dropped back. When Susan looked over her shoulder, she saw no sign of them. She guessed they were laying false scents, confusing the trail. Their own way was on a grassy strip beside the river. But soon the ground began to rise. The forest climbed with it, close on their right, towering and impenetrable − at least, she would have thought so, but after more than an hour's steady running, Brand turned without warning and plunged into it. The moonlight could not break through and the world suddenly darkened. But Susan felt no threat, even though it was colder in here and the trees pressed close, for Brand was obviously at home. He began to hum a tune as he jogged along. After a time he slowed his pace to a walk and waited till Susan and Nick came up with him. They were on top of a mound almost bare of growth, their faces level with the heads of the trees.

'This is Wildwood,' Brand said, waving his arm. 'She is mother to us all – all Woodlanders.'

'Were you born here?' Susan asked.

'I was born here. I shall die in here. For me there is no other world than Wildwood. I know every tree. I know every blade of grass. They are my brothers and sisters.'

Susan smiled. She knew what he meant. 'How big is it?'

'Look,' Brand said. The sky was lightening. Dawn was coming over the mountains. The black forest stretched out towards the west. Shreds of mist rose among the trees. 'That way, two days' walk as far as Sheercliff. The Sweet Water flows along its edge. That was the river you crossed. Once it was sweet right down to the sea. Now, after it tumbles over Sheercliff, we call it Poison. Poison Water.' His eyes held a bitter sadness. He shook himself. 'Well, Marna will tell you that story. You ask me how big Wildwood is? Two days to Sheercliff. And three days back the other way to the mountains. But south, down there,' he pointed into the distance, 'more walking than even I have done. It is high summer now. Deep in winter you would still be in Wildwood. Yet that too Otis Claw and his Halfmen seek to conquer.'

'Who is Otis Claw? What are Halfmen?'

'No. No. It is Marna's tale. Dawn is here. We must stay in the trees.' He led them down from the knoll into the shadows. They drank from a stream and ate dried fern roots from Brand's bag. Then they ran again. Susan could not see any path. Brand seemed to turn left or right without any reason. Yet always the ground rose and Susan guessed they were heading towards the mountains. Once they would find the tunnel again and she and Nick could go back to their world.

When the sun was overhead Brand called a halt. The place was a grassy bank beside a stream. How beautiful it would have been, Susan thought, if everything had not been grey. She drank from her cupped hands and ate more of Brand's food. It still had no taste. This world *should* have been beautiful, everything was there to make it beautiful, yet it was dull, dead, colourless. It was like food with no salt in it. She lay down on the grass and tried to sleep. Soon the rest of the Woodlanders came up with them. They were laughing, chattering. Their eyes should be glowing, Susan thought, and their furry cheeks should be coloured – but no, they were grey, like everything else.

'Odo Cling will be at his camp,' Brand said. 'He will be armed and starting out again. By nightfall Deathguards will be on our trail. But we have a day's march on them. Walt, where did you make your trail?'

'I led them to the gorges,' grinned a man.

'Breeze?'

A woman smiled. 'I to the vanishing stream.'

'Dale?'

'To the hundred caverns.'

'Verna?'

'I took them south, to the place of giant trees.'

'Good. We shall gain many hours. Now Susan and Nick must rest awhile. By tomorrow nightfall we must reach Marna's cave.'

Susan lay back in the soft grey grass. It lapped about her face. Overhead, small birds, shaped like teardrops, darted in the leaves. They were like rainbirds, she thought, like grey warblers. Their thin sweet song came pattering down like rain. It was the first beautiful sound she had heard in this world.

55

'Nick,' she whispered, 'that was clever of you – calling like a morepork.'

Nick was lying on his elbow. He grinned at her. 'Good, eh?' he boasted. 'They've got this bird that sounds a bit like a morepork so I thought I'd send you a warning. Old Brand nearly had a fit.'

'Is this world a dream?'

'No. It's real all right. The planet O. I haven't worked it out yet. I thought it might be some sort of alternate world – but the moon is different, and the stars. So we must have travelled out somewhere into the Milky Way.'

'How did you get here?'

'I pinched Jimmy Jaspers' bottle and had a sniff. I think what happens is – they've got some sort of force-field in there, in the mineshaft. When you sniff that stuff it drags you in. Then it breaks you down somehow, into molecules maybe, or impulses, and you go through a warp. It puts you together again when you come out the other side. I'd sooner travel by train.'

'Nick – they stabbed Jimmy Jaspers. Odo Cling's guards.'

'I know. I saw.'

'He wanted me to save him.'

'Some cheek. Still, it was pretty nasty. I heard them fighting as I came up the tunnel. The bloke with the knife stabbed him twice. There was nothing I could do. He was still breathing when I got to him, but then he stopped. Brand's people took him away. I suppose they buried him somewhere.'

'Was it you I saw moving?'

'Yes. I waved. It was a risk, but I wanted you to see. I was going to follow, but then Brand came, and Breeze and Walt and the others. They've been keeping a watch on Odo Cling. I told them about Jimmy Jaspers. I told them about your mark, Sue. That made them pretty excited. I wonder what it is.'

'When I touch people it's as if they get a shock of electricity.'

'I know. I saw Odo Cling. And that guard. It was as if they'd been hit by a bus.'

'Thank you for rescuing me.'

'Thank Brand. They're fantastic trackers. They almost turn themselves into trees or rocks. Brand was in those boulders when you tried to escape. He was close enough to touch you. And you saw them when they came last night. One of them was right under the sentry's nose when the moon came out and he just seemed to shape himself like a stone.'

Brand's voice said, 'Enough talk. Try to sleep. We've got hard travelling ahead.'

'I can't sleep,' Susan said. 'My wrists hurt where they tied me. And my cheek. Odo Cling hit me with his whip.'

Brand made a sound of annoyance. 'Ah. Yes. Foolish. I should have thought. Breeze.'

But the woman had heard. Already she had darted into the trees.

'Breeze has been taught by Marna,' Brand said.

In a moment the woman came back. She knelt by Susan and looked at her cheek. 'Yes,' she said, 'Halfmen ropes burn like fire. And Odo Cling has a whip made of Bloodcat hide. It cuts deep. But this will take away the pain and leave no scar.' She held a fruit shaped like a lemon and two or three small pointed leaves. She bit the fruit neatly in half, laid the leaves inside, and closed it up. 'This was taught me by Marna. Even a heart wound can be healed by this.' She held the fruit a moment, then opened it. The body of the leaves had been eaten away and skeletons remained. Breeze picked them off. Then she dipped her finger in the juice of the fruit and smeared it gently on Susan's cheek.

'There. The pain should go.'

'It does. It feels like – warm oil.'

'Now your wrists.'

'Don't touch the birthmark.'

Breeze laughed. 'Oh, we are not Halfmen. See?' She laid

her palm on the mark. 'Only those who have lost their natures shall be harmed.' She smeared juice on the rope-burns. The pain went away. 'Now you can sleep. But never eat this fruit. Or the leaves. Only when they are brought together do they become whole.'

Susan sighed. She felt peaceful now the pain was gone. 'Thank you. This would be a beautiful world if everything wasn't grey.'

Breeze stared at her. Her face showed consternation. She turned angrily on Brand. 'Foolish man, she is still unsighted. Why did you not say?'

'I did not know. But I should have thought. She sniffed the yellow smoke, like Nick. Can you find some Shy?'

'Yes. There is a place. Two hours away. Verna and I will go. Sleep, Susan. When I come back you shall see our world.'

'What –'

'Sleep.'

She signalled the girl Verna, and the two darted down the stream and vanished like shadows in the grey trunks of the trees.

'Nick?'

'I'm tired too, Susan. Just get ready for colours you've never seen.' He lay back in the grass and closed his eyes. Susan lay back too. She felt as if she was in a feather-bed. Tiredness pressed on her like heavy weights and she fell at once into a dreamless sleep. When she woke the sun had moved down the sky. It was warm on the side of her face. She felt for the mark of Odo Cling's whip but it had gone. She smiled and sat up.

'Nick.'

He was drinking at the stream. He came up to her with Brand, who gave her a piece of dried root from his pouch.

'Wait for Breeze,' Nick said. 'Then you'll be able to taste it.'

'I feel better now. Nick, we'll have to get back. Mum and

Dad are going to be worried crazy. And your parents.' She looked at Brand. 'Will we be able to go through the tunnel again?'

The Woodlander looked uncomfortable. He lowered his eyes. 'I don't know. We must talk with Marna first. She knows all secrets.'

'Who's Marna?'

'She must tell you that. Here is Breeze. See, she has the Shy.'

Breeze and Verna came up the stream towards them. Although they had been running for two hours they still had the quick Woodlander movement. Breeze was smiling. She held something cupped in her hand and when she came to Susan she held it out. 'The Shy. The rarest plant in Wildwood. It will cure your blindness.'

'I'm not blind.'

'You are unsighted. The yellow smoke did that. Nick was unsighted too, but I gave him Shy. Now he can see.' She opened her fingers and Susan saw a plain little grey flower lying on her palm. It was shaped like a snowdrop. Susan was disappointed. She had expected something wonderful; although, she thought, the name Shy should have warned her. She wondered how this dull little flower could help her.

'Take it,' Breeze said. 'We found a patch of ten, and said the prayer and made the apology. Now it is yours.'

Susan took the flower. She laid it awkwardly on her palm. 'What do I do?'

'Hold it in your fingers. Smell it the way you would smell a rose. The Shy will release its scent. It lasts only a moment. Breathe in deep.'

Susan was nervous. She remembered the yellow smoke and wanted no more magic of that kind. But she trusted these people. Breeze had healed her. So, with an uncertain smile, she lifted the flower to her nose and breathed in. For a moment nothing happened, she smelt nothing. Then something seemed to break in the flower. A waft of perfume rose about her face. It was cold as snow and delicate as a breeze, sweet yet astringent, like lemon blossom. It raced through her quick as water, reaching through her brain and through her body. It set everything singing and vibrating. The world in front of her sprang out like a darkened room when the light goes on. Susan gave a cry of wonder and delight. Wildwood stood before her in its colours. The sun rolled yellow in the sky. The trees were like green and golden cities. Bright birds fluttered in their upper levels. The stream was transparent blue, the grass was green, and berries bright as lipstick clustered on the bushes. She looked at her palm – her own pink palm – and the Shy lay there, bright blue as the sky.

Nick was grinning at her. 'Better than colour TV.'

'Oh, Nick, it's wonderful. I never want to leave.' There were colours she had never seen and could not name. And when she looked at Breeze and Verna she saw their skins were a beautiful muted colour, like red copper. Their hair, their fur, had folds of gold and green and bronze, and their eyes shone with a mysterious colour – violet or blue? 'You're both so beautiful. And I thought you were grey.'

Breeze smiled. But she looked sad. 'See the Shy is dying. It has given scent and now its life is done.'

Susan looked. The flower in her palm was fading, wilting. Its petals began to curl. Breeze untied a small green bag from her throat. She took the dying flower and put it inside. It was these bags, Susan guessed, that the Woodlanders had used to overcome the Halfmen.

'The Shy has uses,' Breeze said, 'even when it withers. It is too much for Halfmen.'

'Thank you,' Susan said. 'I'm sorry it had to die.'

'I'm sorry too. We do not pick the Shy unless the need is great. I hope you will not fail us, Susan.'

Susan did not know what she meant by that. But she shook her head, knowing she had to make a return – the colours, the scents and sounds of Wildwood still overwhelmed her.

'Eat your fern root,' Nick said.

Susan looked at it. It was golden-brown. She put it to her mouth and took a bite. The taste was delicious. Nick was right – bananas, but vanilla too and walnuts. She ate greedily.

Brand said, 'Now she will travel better. Let us move.' His fur had the same copper colour as the women's. His eyes were a deep blue. Everything had changed – the robes were a shadowy green and earthy brown. She looked at her own. She looked at her birthmark. A brown teardrop, a plum-red drop, folding into each other, as though they were lovers – or enemies. She looked at them and felt afraid.

The little band set off again at a steady jog-trot. Nick and Susan ran side by side, following Brand, with Breeze and Verna at their backs. They went on through the afternoon, moving easily. Susan felt she had the strength to run to the ends of the forest and over the mountains. Brand led them on a way that climbed. From time to time they came out of the trees and moved across the tops of grassy knolls. Looking back, Susan saw the forest shimmering and breathing under the sun. Further off, an oily iridescent haze marked the lowlands where the Halfmen lived. She wondered where Odo Cling was. She pictured him and his guards following along their trail, sniffing like dogs.

'What does Odo Cling look like?' she asked Nick.

'Black and grey. He doesn't change.'

At nightfall they ate and drank again and Susan lay down on a bed of fern Breeze made for her and slept without dream or movement till dawn. She went to the stream beside the camp and washed. She was anxious to be away. Something told her Odo Cling had come much closer in the night. But when she told this fear to Brand he laughed. 'No. He is far away. Cling and his men have followed our false trails.'

All day they travelled at the same hard pace. Now and then a view of mountains opened up ahead. But the forest went on, even though patches of snowgrass grew in the clearings. At midday Dale and Walt climbed into trees – ran up them like monkeys – and came down with fruit shaped like butter-nuts, and baked them in the embers of a fire. They had the taste of sweet potatoes. Verna brought Susan a handful of blue berries that tasted like guavas. She shared them with Nick through the afternoon.

The sun was a red ball in the Darkland haze when they came to a high rock wall blocking their path. But Brand made no hesitation. He climbed a dozen steps, pushed through some brambles, and vanished. Nick and Susan followed and found themselves in a narrow passage set with mosses and small flowering plants. Brand beckoned them. They went along a track between walls and after several minutes came out into a valley shaped like a cup, with a grassy floor and trees growing down the sides. A wide-mouthed cave opened at the side of a trickling stream. By the cave an old woman in a blue robe stood and waited.

'That is Marna,' Brand said.

'Who is she?'

'Marna. Wife of Freeman Wells. She is the one who knows. Come, Susan. She is waiting for you. She has waited many years.'

They crossed the stream and walked over the springy grass to the cave. Marna watched them. Her deep eyes made no sign of welcome, but burned with emotions that set her trembling – fear, Susan thought, and exultation, and some-thing like love, devotion – was it worship? She stopped, con-fused.

'Come, child. Close to me. Do not be afraid.'

'I'm not afraid.'

'No, you are not. I see. But you have many questions. I have answers. It is time for you to know what you must do. Show me the Mark.'

Susan went forward slowly. Nick kept at her side and she

62

was glad. She reached out and held his hand. Marna was strange – strange in some hidden unnatural way – stranger even than Odo Cling; and though she was not afraid she felt a deep unwillingness to hear what it was the woman had to say. She felt it might simply be a cry of love or anguish.

She came close to Marna. Cautiously she raised her hand and showed her wrist. The birthmark seemed to glow in the fading light. And Marna's eyes burned bright. She bent close to the mark. She raised a stick-thin finger, brought it close, just as Odo Cling had done. But in a moment she stopped and drew it away.

'Yes, yes,' she said in a strange light voice, 'it is the Mark. You are the one. I have seen it before and will never forget.' Tears ran from her eyes and dropped on Susan's wrist. There was a sadness here deeper than any Susan had ever seen, and she felt an urgent desire to comfort Marna and make her happy. She did not know how.

'You can touch it,' she whispered.

'What?' the old woman said.

'Please touch it if you want to. If it will help.'

'Help?'

'Don't be frightened. It won't hurt. It only hurts the Halfies.'

Marna laughed. It was a sound soft and calm but infinitely sad. She touched Susan gently on the brow. 'Thank you, Susan. Thank you, child. But no, I cannot touch. I am not a Woodlander. I am not like Brand and Breeze and Verna. Ah, no. Darkland is the place where I was born. I am like Otis Claw and Odo Cling. I am a Halfie.'

5

Marna

The children and Breeze and Brand ate their meal in Marna's cave. She fed them soup ladled from a pot bubbling on a fire. They drank water flavoured with berry juice. Nick and Susan looked about curiously as they ate. The cave was deep and high-ceilinged. It was lit by flames burning in frosty globes. Alcoves ran off to the sides, curtained with woven cloths.

'It is my hospital,' Marna said.

'She is healer to the Woodlanders,' Breeze explained. 'When we have broken bones or pains or fevers, or one of us has been mauled by a cat, our friends carry us here and Marna heals us. It was Marna who discovered the Shy.'

The old woman smiled. 'I found it, and my husband, Freeman Wells, discovered its use. It was Shy that opened the passage between the worlds. When you go back Shy will make your path.'

'I thought it was the yellow smoke,' Nick said.

'Ah yes,' the old woman looked unhappy. 'The yellow smoke. That is the invention of Otis Claw. Otis Claw was a pupil of Freeman Wells. It was Otis Claw who broke the balance. But eat and drink, then I will tell the story. I must look at my patients.'

She went off into the alcoves and soon her voice came murmuring out, and once she sang a lullaby so sweet and restful that Nick and Susan felt their eyes begin to close. Marna came back. She had a happier look, as though caring for the sick had lifted her troubles. Her white hair lay in braids upon her back. Her skin had a red-gold glow.

She said to Susan, 'One of my patients wishes to talk with you.'

'Who?'

'Come and see. He has been close to death. He wishes you to know that he is sorry.'

'Nick?'

'Yes,' he said, 'I'll come. It can only be him.'

And it was Jimmy Jaspers, lying on a low bed in one of the alcoves. He seemed to be shrunken to half his size. Bandages covered the wounds in his chest. His hands lay at his sides but when he saw Susan he held them out. He tried to twist his lumpy face in a smile.

'Sit down, girlie. No? Well, I don't blame yer. I done some bad things in me time but that was the bloddy worst. You too, younker,' he said to Nick, breathing painfully. 'Guess I would've done the same to you. Sent the pair of yer off to the works like a couple of bobby calves.'

Susan stopped clear of the reach of his hands. She did not know whether she was glad to see him or not. 'I thought you were dead.'

'I woulda been. They stuck me like a pig. But them little sheilas in green dresses give me some stuff to swaller. Saved me life, I reckon. Carried me down on a kind of stretcher. Give me to old nursey here.' He waved at Marna. 'She knows a thing or two. Give me some bloddy flower ter sniff and I seen what a ratbag I am.'

'Is he going to be all right?' Susan said to Marna.

'Yes. The wounds were deep. But Breeze was there in time. He nearly died, but by tomorrow evening he will be well.'

'Then I'm headin' orf after Odo Cling. I'm gunner twist 'is lyin' head orf 'is shoulders.'

'I thought you might like to come back with us — to our world,' Susan said.

'Sure I will. When I've stomped 'im into the ground.'

Marna sighed. 'I have never known good and evil to battle so in a man. Jimmy Jaspers, do you not see, revenge will not bring you happiness? You will let the evil triumph in you.'

'Just fer five minutes, I will. That's how long it'll take fer me ter settle things with 'im. Then I'll be good. Promise yer, nursey. I'll even stop lickin' me plate.' He coughed and a spasm of pain crossed his face. 'Wish I 'ad some whisky. Or else a cuppa tea. This blackberry juice yer feedin' me tastes like lolly water.'

'It has kept you alive. And you have had enough talk now. I will give you something to make you sleep.' She shepherded Susan and Nick back to the curtain.

'Girl,' Jimmy Jaspers said. Susan turned. 'I'm sorry. I done some pretty hairy things in me time. Jumped a claim. Stole a horse from me mate. Smash-an'-grabbed a jeweller's shop once. Did time for that one too. But sellin' kids. That's the bloddy worst. I'll never do that again.'

'All right,' Susan said. 'We'll see you in the morning.' She still did not like Jimmy Jaspers. She had no doubt he was more bad than good. But somehow seeing him gave her a feeling that in the end everything would be all right. She supposed it was because, like Nick, he came out of her own world. Dropping the curtain on his alcove, she suddenly felt sick with longing for home; the farm, the house, her bedroom and her bed, and especially her parents.

'Nick,' she whispered, 'I want to go home.'

'Me too. Trouble is, I want to stay here as well.'

They sat down with Brand and Breeze at the fire. In a moment Marna joined them. 'He has gone to sleep. Do not be frightened of him, Susan. Shy has helped him find the good in himself. He will not harm you.'

'He'll harm Odo Cling,' Nick said.

'Ah yes. He is full of rage and hatred, and turns it all on Cling. But it will not be enough. Next to Cling he is a child. He does not understand what evil is.'

Susan shivered. Coldness seemed to slide into the cave. She hunched close to the fire. 'Who is Odo Cling? And Otis Claw? And this mark on my wrist? What is it? And the man who came when I was born? I know it seems impossible but I remember him.'

Marna smiled sadly. 'That was a beginning for you, but for him it was the end.'

'Who was he?'

'Freeman Wells. My husband. He has never returned. Perhaps he wanders lost in your world still.'

'No,' Nick said. Then he wished he had not spoken. Marna and Breeze and Brand had fixed him with looks on which he felt himself squirming like an insect on a pin.

'What do you know, Nick?' Brand said quietly.

'I heard my uncle and aunt talking about the night he came. There was a storm. He put the mark on Susan and ran away. Uncle Ted found him after the storm. He was – dead. He'd fallen down a cliff and broken his neck. At least, that's what Uncle Ted thought. But Jimmy Jaspers said the Halfies killed him.'

'Yes,' Susan said. She was close to weeping. 'I waited all my life – and all the time he was dead.'

Marna sighed. For a moment her eyes had burned; now they grew dull. 'I have told myself he might be living, but it has never been a real hope. I felt his death in my heart. He would have found some way to return.'

Breeze took her hand. In a soft voice, she began to sing. It was a slow song, full of falling notes. Soon Brand joined in, and at last Marna added her voice. Even the fire seemed to darken. Grief trembled in the air. Then from out of those heavy notes a melody began to grow. Grief remained, but resignation held a place there too; and in the end gladness moved as lightly as a bird, soaring away from the sorrow and darkness of the earth. Listening, wiping their eyes, the children knew that Freeman Wells had found his rest.

The voices fell silent. The singers let their joined hands fall apart. Brand put wood on the fire. Breeze poured berry juice in the cups.

'That song will be sung while Wildwood lasts. Don't be unhappy, Susan. He lived a life that gave hope to us all.'

'Yes. But – I wish I could have met him.'

Marna stirred. 'You did meet him.'

'I suppose you're right.'

'And Nick. Thank you for your news. Now I can put away my hope and go on with my task.' She turned to Susan. 'That is to tell this child what she must do.'

'Can't I go home?' Susan said.

'Let me tell my tale. Then you will decide.'

'All right.'

'I shall have to go back to the beginnings. You have seen our world? You have seen O? How beautiful it is?'

'Yes.'

'Humans have always lived in Darkland – though once it had another name, Manhome. And Waterfolk in the rivers and seas. Woodlanders in Wildwood. Birdfolk beyond the mountains, and Stonefolk under them. That is the way it has been from the beginning. So the story goes. Each folk has its history. And each its dispensation. There have been troubles. And trouble now – greater trouble than the land has known – comes from Humankind.'

'The Halfies,' Nick said.

'We have not always been Halfies. Only for nineteen turns of our globe. In the beginning, in the ancient days, Humankind tore themselves apart. There was no law, only chaos. Nothing comes from that time but a memory in the blood. Then a wise one came. Some call him Firstman, some Freeman. He found law in chaos. He looked in Man and saw there Good and Evil, and he gave them names and understood them. Then there was a moment when knowledge gave him powers that some would call magical, and others call divine. Some say there is a Creator who used him as an instrument. I cannot say. But Freeman, Firstman, made the Motherstone, and laid the Halves on it, and put Humankind in balance. Chaos stopped. History began. And Humankind lived for many thousands of years free to choose the evil or the good. Alas, there have been countless evil times, vile ambitions dressed up in great names. War and oppression stain the centuries. But the Balance held. The Halves lay on the Motherstone and Humankind stayed in tune with Freeman's Law. Light and dark contended and held each other in a deep embrace. Yes Susan, that is it, you have the mark on you. There, on your wrist. See how the light bends into the dark, see how dark leans into the light. They hold each other, good and evil. And see, if you look close, in the light there is a spot of dark, and in the dark there is a spot of light.'

The children looked. 'I see,' Nick whispered.

'Yes,' Susan said. 'And together they make a perfect circle.'

'That is Man. That is Freeman's Law.'

'Who broke it?'

'Ah. We come to that. Who robbed the Motherstone? Who broke the Balance?'

'Was it Odo Cling?'

'Oh, not him. Cling is evil, yes. But Cling is a midget, Cling is a yapping dog alongside his master, Otis Claw.'

'So it was him? It was Otis Claw?'

The name had a dreadful sound. It scraped across their minds like a rusty knife.

'It was him. But first I will tell about the one who taught him, Freeman Wells.'

'Freeman Wells? He taught him?'

'Yes, Susan. Always there was a group, wise men, wise women, gathered about the Stone, tending and protecting it, for there were those who wished to destroy it, thinking that way they would rule Humankind. The wisest of the wise had always been given the name Freewoman or Freeman, after the great maker of the Balance. Freeman Wells was wisest in his time. And first among his pupils was a youth called Otis Hand. A golden boy, brilliant and beautiful, who learned

69

the lore of the Stone through the pores of his skin. Soon his wisdom seemed to match that of Freeman Wells. And Freeman Wells trusted him like a son. He left Otis Hand in charge of the Freeband about the Stone, and journeyed to the Upland with his wife, I, Marna, and lived in Wildwood many years, studying the ways of the Woodlanders. We came to love Wildwood. We learned many things. We found the Shy, and learned its uses, and Freeman Wells opened the path to your world.

'Many years went by. And here in Wildwood we lived so happily that Freeman Wells forgot his duty to the Stone. And I forgot. And so we gave Otis Hand all the time he needed. He studied well. Ha! He studied wickedly. He had tasted power, and the seed of evil grew in him, and swelled in him, until he was nothing but a smiling face, a fair exterior, fitted over evil. He saw the land of O, he saw the world, and wanted it for his. He saw Humankind, and saw the seas, and Wildwood, and the mountains, and their Folk, and saw that everything was free. That he could not bear, so he plotted to enslave them and possess them. But first he must destroy Freeman's Law. He must break the Balance, pull the Halves apart. And so he studied, so he delved into the Lore – and found a way.'

Marna's voice had become a grieving sing-song. She drew the tale from deep within herself and every word gave her dreadful pain. The children listened, terrified, appalled.

'There came a day when we in Wildwood, Freeman Wells and I, felt a cleaving in ourselves. We fell down in a sickness and we screamed in agony as nature broke apart in us and the Balance broke. When the pain and fever left we stood and looked at Halfies. We were Halfmen. All through Manhome, all through O, wherever humans lived, it was the same. Woodlanders were unchanged. And Birdfolk, and Stonefolk, and the People of the Sea. They had their own Law. But Humankind were changed, utterly, utterly changed. They were Halfmen.

70

'We knew what had happened. We needed no one to tell us. Otis Hand had learned a way to violate the Stone. Otis Hand had wrenched the Halves from their deep embrace, and in every man and woman in O, good had fought with evil, one last fight, until one or the other was driven out. We had no doubt which would be the stronger. We knew that down in Manhome, Darkland now, Darkland from that instant, the hordes in whom Evil had triumphed hunted down and murdered the unresisting Good. We were good. I say it with no pride. There is no pride in being half. Good must be won daily in the battle that never ends.

'I stayed in Wildwood. Freeman Wells prepared himself and ventured down to Darkland. There he saw the ruler on his throne. The hand with which he had wrenched the Halves from the Motherstone was blasted to a claw, and now in his evil pride he took that name: Otis Claw. Darksoul. The Paingiver. His servant Odo Cling stood trembling at his side – trembling with his eagerness to kill. Freeman Wells walked into the throne-room. They rushed at him with spears and knives. But Freeman Wells had called up all his knowledge and his strength and wove Good about himself and even Otis Claw could not break through. He, my husband, Freeman Wells, tore the Halves from round Claw's neck, where he had hung them like a pretty toy. He saw how Claw's men had attacked the Motherstone with fire and acid – and about the Stone he placed a dome of force no ordinary person can ever break. Only one bearing the Mark, bearing the reborn Halves, can enter there. The dome of force will receive and welcome. All others it throws back, though Claw has tried for nineteen turns to break it.

'Then he fled, my husband. He gave his strength to the dome and oh how spent he then became and vulnerable. He fled to Wildwood, with Odo Cling and the Deathguard at his back. They hunted him. For seven turns of O they hunted. But always he escaped. The Woodlanders sheltered him. The

Birdfolk, the Stonefolk, gave him refuge. Always he studied, always he worked, to save the dying Halves, and put life back in them. At last he found a way and it was done. Then Freeman Wells sought a way to come to the Stone and place the Halves again. But Claw had built a prison round it. He had sunk his Pit into the earth, into living rock, and there in the great hall it lies, half a mile deep, the Motherstone, surrounded always by two rows of guards with iron spears, one row facing in, the other out. Safe in its dome of force, but forever guarded by the chosen men of Otis Claw. And Claw sits on his throne and watches it.

'Freeman Wells could not come to it. Again he fled. Odo Cling and his guards were close. Deep in Wildwood, Freeman Wells took the Halves and placed them on his arm and burned the Mark. Then he journeyed to Stonegut Deep, down into the bowels of O, and found the Stonefolk there and gave the sleeping Half into their care – the Dark Half. They have sworn never to give it up, except to one who comes wearing the Mark. They have taken the Oath. Then Freeman Wells came up from the Deep, and made his way to Morninghall in the Yellow Plains, and there he gave the Light Half into the care of the Birdfolk. They too took the Oath, and keep it to this day – never to surrender the Half except to one who wears the Mark.'

Marna stopped. She looked at Susan sadly. Susan felt herself shrinking.

'I'm the one,' she stammered. 'I'm the wearer of the Mark.'

'Yes. I'm sorry, child. This burden should not have been placed on you. You are not even of this world. But Freeman Wells had no choice. He found no other way.'

Nick was shifting impatiently. 'He must have had. Why Susan? There's a whole world of people here. There are all the Woodlanders. And the Stonefolk and the Birdfolk, whatever they are.'

'No,' Marna said, 'I have told you Nick, the Woodlanders

72

and the other Folk do not come under Freeman's Law. They cannot wear the Mark. And as for people, as for a world full of humans, no, you forget, only Halfmen were left. The Good would have served, but all the Good were slain.'

'Except you.'

'Except me. And I would have been willing to wear the Mark. But Freeman Wells knew that one so old would never have the strength to come to the Stone. He told me of your world – he had been through. It was a world not under the Law, but men lived there in a natural state, a balance held. He hoped to recruit a band of young women and young men, and place the Mark on them and bring them through, and one, he hoped, would find a way to reach the Stone.'

'All right,' Nick said, 'why didn't he?'

'Odo Cling was too close. And Otis Claw had made the yellow smoke. So Halfmen followed Freeman Wells into your world. There was a storm, you say. But for that he might have got away. As it was, he had only time to place the Mark on one.'

'A baby,' Nick burst out. 'How stupid can you get?'

Breeze said, 'Do not speak that way of Freeman Wells. What he found himself able to do, he did. There was no choice.'

'I remember him,' Susan said. 'He was small. He had a beard. He was very sad. He said he was sorry.'

'A baby couldn't understand that,' Nick said.

'He didn't say it in words. And I understood.'

Nick turned to Marna. 'Why haven't they caught her before this? They've had twelve years?'

'They could not breathe your air for more than a moment. So they looked for an agent – and got Jimmy Jaspers in the end. He soon found you, Susan. He told me what happened on that day.'

'What is it you want her to do?' Nick said.

Marna smiled sadly. When she spoke she seemed almost

to weep. 'Go to the Birdfolk and to the Stonefolk. Show the Mark. Claim the Halves. Lay them in their place on the Motherstone.'

'Through two rows of guards with iron spears?' Nick sneered.

Tears ran down Marna's face. 'Yes. It is impossible. Freeman Wells has failed.' Her tears dropped hissing into the fire.

'No,' Breeze said; and Brand shook his head and said, 'While there is one who wears the Mark our world has hope.'

'However young,' Breeze said. She took Susan's hand. 'Freeman Wells must have seen the strength in you. Otherwise he would not have placed the Mark, whatever his danger.'

'Strong babies,' Nick said. He felt he was the only sane one in the cave. He looked at Brand and Breeze, at their coloured fur and red-gold skin and pleading eyes, and looked at Susan, shrinking by the fire, and knew that if he did not do something she was going to say yes and get herself killed.

'Listen Susan, this isn't our world. They've got to fix it themselves. I came through to take you back and that's what I'm going to do. In the morning we're going to the mine and we're going home.'

'Nick –'

'Remember your Mum and Dad. And my parents too.'

There was silence in the cave. Then Marna said, 'You can choose your time of arrival when you go back. You can spend the full summer in O, and all the winter too, and walk out into your world with ten seconds gone. Or a thousand years.' She sighed. 'So, choose an hour. Your parents will not have missed you.'

Nick looked at her. It was probably true. O was like that. But nothing was solved. 'I'm sorry. But if Susan doesn't get out Odo Cling will kill her. We're going home.'

'No, Nick,' Susan said.

'I'm in charge. This isn't a dream. If they stick those knives in you you're going to feel it. Let's get some sleep. We'll make an early start.'

'No,' Brand said. They looked at him. Nick opened his mouth to argue; but Brand said, 'It's not that easy. By now Odo Cling has guards at the mine. The way is closed. He will have done that first, before starting after us.'

Nick looked at him bitterly. 'You knew that was going to happen. We could have got there in time.'

Brand nodded. 'Yes, I knew. But Susan had to come to Marna first. They had to talk.'

'Yes, Nick,' Susan said. 'I had to hear the story. I've been waiting all my life.'

'We're stuck here now. At least until they catch us. Then we're dead.'

'Nick, Odo Cling said they'll take their armies through and conquer Earth. So if we help on O we'll be helping our world too.'

'They can't do that. They can't breathe our air. They can't even breathe the air properly up here.'

Marna said quietly, 'You have looked at Darkland. You have seen the grey cloud over it.'

'Smog,' Nick said. 'So what?'

'The Dark Halfmen are able to see no colour. They can taste nothing. Many things they have lost. I believe they do not know the seasons. And clean air in their lungs causes them pain. But Otis Claw is making air they can breathe. He makes it in great factories. Already it covers Darkland. It has climbed half-way up Sheercliff. One day it will cover all of Wildwood, all the mountains. Then Otis Claw will have our world. He will turn to yours. He will pump Halfman air through the passage. There will be no way you can stop it. When your world is poisoned, then he will send his Halfman army through. That is the plan.'

Breeze took Susan's hand. 'All that stands in his way is you, Susan.'

Again there was silence. Susan stared at the fire. Nick put his face in his hands. He hunted desperately for an argument, but could not find one. At last he heard Susan say, 'I'll do it. I'll try to do it. Nick will help.'

'Yes,' he heard himself say. 'I'll do my best.'

'Then all is not lost,' Marna said. 'Tomorrow we will plan what we must do. Now it is late. Let us all sleep. We must be fresh.'

She showed Nick and Susan into alcoves. She gave them drinks that soothed their fears and made them sleep. Dawn light was seeping into the cave when a sound woke them. There was a calling of voices outside, and someone came running into the cave.

'Marna! Brand!'

The children jumped from their beds and pulled the curtains aside. The Woodlander Dale was in the cave. Brand and Breeze and Marna came hurrying from their beds.

Dale fell to his knees, panting with distress. 'Odo Cling is coming. He has a hundred men. He has a Bloodcat.'

6

Bloodcat

'Stand,' Marna commanded, and Dale came to his feet. Marna stepped close to him and looked at his heaving chest and working face. She placed the palms of her hands on his temples.

'Be calm.'

Dale obeyed. His distress vanished. Still urgently, but without letting his fear show, he said, 'I was scouting down the trail. I heard the screaming of the Cat. It was dark. They were marching in the night. Then in the dawn I saw them. Odo Cling. A hundred men. I counted. And the Cat. A female. Fully grown. Odo Cling held her on a leash.'

'How close are they?' Brand asked.

'An hour. Maybe less. They did not see me. I came fast. But we must be gone.'

Brand darted outside. The children heard him calling commands to the Woodlanders.

'I heard they could tame Bloodcats,' Breeze said. 'I did not believe it.'

'They do not tame them,' Marna said. 'The Cats recognize a blood-lust greater than their own. They are cowed, and so they serve.'

Breeze shook her head. 'But even a Cat should not have been able to follow us. We left false trails.'

'It followed Susan,' Marna said.

'How?'

Marna turned to Susan. 'Child, did you leave anything? Any piece of clothing?'

'No,' Susan said, feeling cold with fear.

'I know,' Nick said. 'The rope we cut off her wrists. It had blood on it.'

'That would be enough. The Bloodcat took the scent from that. So your false trails served no purpose.'

Breeze groaned. 'How could we know they would bring a Cat?'

'You must get your patients away,' Dale said to Marna. 'How many can walk?'

'All but Jimmy Jaspers.'

'We will carry him,' Breeze said. 'Susan, Nick, take some food from the pot. Drink. You must travel fast today.'

'We cannot escape a Bloodcat,' Marna said. 'Not with a litter to carry. Not with sick ones in the party. And an old woman slowing us down.'

'But we must try.' Breeze went about the alcoves, rousing the patients. Jimmy Jaspers cried out querulously. She soothed him. Brand came in.

'Come. You must be gone. We will fight them down the trail. It will give you a little time.'

'No,' Marna said. 'They will kill you all.'

'There is no other way.'

Marna smiled sadly. 'Brand, I have secrets you do not know. There is a way. But do I have the strength? I do not know. And Wildwood is not mine. I must have permission.'

'Ask.'

Marna turned to Susan and Nick. 'Wash at the stream. Take blankets, food. You must travel into the mountains. It is cold. Farewell. Do not fail us.'

'Won't we see you again?'

'There will be no time for speaking. Go. Remember me. And forgive me and my husband, Freeman Wells.'

Breeze came and helped them choose blankets and roll them up. They packed satchels of food and carried them outside. Brand and Marna talked deep in the cave. All the patients were ready and some had gone across the valley and were climbing a path into the hills. Four Woodlanders lifted Jimmy Jaspers on a litter.

'What's all the rush?' Jimmy Jaspers said. 'I was enjoyin' me shuteye. I don't like bein' woke.'

'Odo Cling is coming,' Susan said.

'What are we runnin' for then? I'll wring 'is neck like a sparrer.'

'He's got a hundred men,' Nick said. 'And a Bloodcat.'

'I'm not scared of pussies.' But the strain of talking had made his face go grey. He fell back on the litter and the Woodlanders carried him across the basin and started up the track.

Breeze came to the children.

'Come. We must start.'

'What about Marna?'

'She will come with Brand. Be quick now. Cling is only half an hour away. Verna, lead. I will follow.' They hefted their rolled blankets and satchels of food and started off. As they climbed the hillside Susan looked and saw Brand and Marna coming from the cave. They crossed the grass and walked to the entrance of the track. Marna carried nothing but a staff of wood.

'What's Marna going to do?'

'I don't know,' Breeze said. 'But pray that she does not fail.'

They laboured up the track. It climbed above Marna's cave and then turned back and made a steep diagonal across a hill covered with small trees and slabs of rock. Then it turned into a cleft thickly grown with bush and crossed a wooden bridge over the stream that ran down into the basin by the cave. The shade was cold. Patches of mist hung in the trees. Marna and Brand had fallen farther behind. Susan did not see them as she crossed the bridge or later as she came into sunlight on another hillside beyond the cleft. They climbed steeply again, going up a narrow path that angled back and forth. Ahead, the sick from Marna's hospital trudged slowly on. The Woodlanders battled with Jimmy Jaspers' stretcher. Verna and Breeze and the children came up with them.

'Nick, we're going too slow. We're going to get caught.'

'Then I guess we'll fight.'

'The Bloodcat's following me. If I went off on my own it would save the others.'

'Saint Susan. Don't be wet.'

'They don't want to kill me. They want to capture me.'

'If you don't shut up and keep moving they'll do that soon enough.'

They came to a slab of rock at the top of the hill. Here the patients rested. They were panting with distress. Breeze went among them, giving them medicine from her pack and checking their bandages. Marna and Brand came into view on the zig-zag path. Far below, the cave and basin showed. The sun had not reached them, but it shone on Wildwood, making it vibrate with colours. Beyond lay the brown puddle of Darkland, faintly iridescent in the sun. Breeze and Nick and Susan stood on the edge of the rock, watching for Marna and Brand to come up.

'Soon you will see Odo Cling and the Bloodcat,' Breeze said.

As if in answer, a hideous cry came winding through the air. The pain of it made them cover their ears. It was like a fingernail scraping on a blackboard – but it was filled with hatred and a mindless cruelty. Far below, sunlight came at last to Marna's basin. The stream shone like silver and the grass was suddenly painted green and gold. It was like a jewel, an opal, set on the edge of the forest. But the cry hung over it, a ghastly echo; and the Deathguard came bursting from the wall and scattered like an army of black ants across the grass.

The Bloodcat came, held on a leash by Odo Cling. The sun made it burn like fire. It was not large. It stood no higher than Odo Cling's waist. But even at this distance they could see its awful sinuousness and hideous strength, and feel its blood-lust quivering in the air. It was the colour of an open wound.

'Nick, it's looking at me.'

The Bloodcat raised its head and screamed.

'It can see me. Odo Cling can see me.'

'Easy child,' Breeze said.

Cling raised his arm and pointed, and though he was far away, tiny as a house-fly on a wall, Susan felt he could have reached out and touched her – and that the Bloodcat could have caught her in one bound. Behind her the sick moved off again, urged on by the Woodlanders. But Jimmy Jaspers pushed his bearers aside. He rolled off his litter and heaved himself to his feet. Like a grey old elephant he lumbered to the edge of the rock slab and looked into the basin.

'Cling, yer bloddy twister. I'm gunner get yer, Cling,' he yelled.

'Hush. Go. Your bearers wait,' Breeze said.

'Yer hear me, Cling? I'm gunner tie a knot in yer. I'm gunner ram yer skinny legs down yer throat.'

'Go,' Breeze commanded.

'Keep yer hair on, nursey. I just wanted 'im ter know.' He went back to his litter and lay down.

'Take him. Quick. We do not have much time,' Brand ordered, coming on to the rock. Marna was at his side. She looked into the basin.

'They are looting my cave.'

'Cling lets them have their sport. He knows we cannot get away,' Breeze said.

The Deathguards dragged out beds, curtains, tables, mats – everything that would move. They tore and rent and smashed them, leaping in a frenzy, and heaped them in a mound and set them alight. Smoke rose in the still morning air.

'Now he has them in order. Now he comes.'

'Why are we waiting?' Nick said. 'He'll be here in ten minutes.'

'I shall meet them on the Living Hill,' Marna said. 'Breeze, take them on.'

'Marna,' Susan began, but the old woman stopped her.

'We have made our farewells.'

Below, the Deathguards swarmed into the track, with Odo Cling and the Bloodcat leading. Breeze took Susan by the arm and pulled her over the rock. They started up another path that ran across the hill. Soon they turned the ridge and came up with the stretcher.

'We should be setting an ambush,' Nick said. 'We should be doing something, not just running.'

'Marna has a plan,' Breeze said.

'What can she do? One old woman?'

'This is the Living Hill. She will face them here.'

They had come off the ridge on to a path crossing a slope studded with boulders. It was steep almost as the wall of a house and ran down into the forest half a kilometre below, and up it seemed forever into the sky. It was like a giant slide or chute. The Woodlanders and the patients were making their way across, heading for an abutment on the far side. The stretcher bearers started out, moving with great care. One slip would send them sliding into the forest. Jimmy Jaspers rolled his head and bellowed with alarm.

'Come,' Breeze said, 'and be careful. The path is narrow.'

That, Nick thought, was an understatement. At times it seemed no wider than a piece of string. They moved gingerly, the length of a football field, out into the middle of the slope. 'Are you all right?'

'Yes,' Susan said. She was pale. She clung to tufts of grass and knobs of stone. Below, the tops of the trees looked like knots of dark green wool. Now and then parts of the hillside showed. They seemed to hang in space. But mostly there was only the yellow path and the distant forest floor, and nothing in between.

Ahead of them was a great boulder. There the slope grew easier and the path more safe. They stopped a moment to breathe. The sick had reached the other side. Jimmy Jaspers and his bearers were nearly there.

'You're doing well, Susan,' Verna said.

'I don't like heights.'

'Why do they call this the Living Hill?' Nick asked.

Breeze had come up with them. 'Can you feel it tremble beneath your feet?'

'No.'

'Be still.'

'I feel it now. A kind of small vibration. Feel it, Susan?'

'Yes.'

'So we call it the Living Hill.'

'I don't like it here. Can we go on?'

'Rest a moment. You are safe.'

Susan saw Brand and Marna coming along the ridge towards the Living Hill. 'Do you know what Marna's going to do?'

'I think I can guess,' Breeze said. She laid her hand on the hillside in a gesture that seemed to include gratitude and sadness.

'How can she fight them? And the Bloodcat? She's an old woman.'

'She is old. But there are other strengths. And a single way. Susan, if she fails then we must fight.'

'I know. Can we go on now?'

'Yes. Let us go.'

Down in the cleft where the bush lay thick they heard the Bloodcat screaming.

'How can she fight that?

The rest of the path was easier. In a few moments they joined the Woodlanders and Jimmy Jaspers on the abutment. Marna and Brand had reached the Living Hill and were coming across. The old woman seemed weak on her legs. Brand supported her and urged her on. When they reached the boulder half-way along the path they stopped. Using her staff, supported by Brand, Marna began to climb. She made her way up the slope beside the boulder. Brand went ahead and kept a grip on her, pulling her by her cloak, supporting her when she slipped. At last they came out on the giant boulder, and stood on it where it jutted over the path.

'Why are they stopping there?'

'Brand is not stopping. Marna stops alone.'

'Why there?'

'It is the Keystone.'

'Look,' Nick said, 'there are the Deathguards. There, in the trees.'

They were coming in an ant-line, coming fast. Soon they would be on the ridge, and then on the Living Hill. The Bloodcat glowed like an ember.

'What's Brand waiting for? We've got to get out of here.'

But Brand was not coming. He turned away from Marna. The old woman had slumped down on her knees. 'Breeze,' Brand called, his voice sharp and urgent, 'bring Susan. Marna must speak with her.'

'Come child,' Breeze said. 'Quickly now.'

'She can't go back there,' Nick said.

'She must. Marna needs her.'

'Then I'm coming too.'

'Yes. It does not matter. Let us go.'

With Breeze leading, they hurried back along the path. Brand held Marna's staff down to them and they scrambled on to the Keystone.

'She cannot do it,' Brand said.

Nick had gone to the edge of the boulder. It was like standing on the prow of a ship; or on the nose of a jet-liner, speeding through the air. Far below, the forest seemed to roll back under him and draw him down.

'She cannot kill.'

'I am a Halfwoman,' Marna whispered. 'They left no dark in me. Susan, you must help me.'

'Yes. How?'

'You'll have to hurry,' Nick said. 'Here they come.'

The Deathguard came round the point of the ridge. Their robes flapped as they ran. Odo Cling and the Bloodcat appeared. The Cat gave a scream.

'Come here,' Marna said.

Susan went to her and knelt at her side.

'Give me your wrist. I must touch the mark.'

'No. It'll kill you.'

'I will touch only the dark side. I must take some evil into myself.'

Susan folded her robe back off her wrist. The mark lay there, ordinary, innocent. She had known it all her life. But Marna trembled when she saw it.

'Hurry,' Brand said.

Marna put her hand out and painfully uncurled a finger. She brought it down slowly to the mark. A groan came from her lips. She seemed to force her hand forward against a great repelling force.

'I cannot, child. Help me.'

'Take her hand,' Breeze said.

Susan gripped the old woman's wrist. As firmly as she could she forced it down. Marna's finger touched the blood-red mark. At once she began to writhe and scream.

'Hold it there,' Breeze shouted. 'Do not let her go.'

'It's hurting her.'

'This is what she chose.'

Susan felt something vibrating, humming, in Marna's hand. She felt a live thing, like a lizard, wriggle and slide along the old woman's wrist under her skin.

'Oh-uh, oh-uh,' Marna screamed. They were cries of terrible pain and grief.

'Enough,' Breeze said. She rushed forward and knocked Marna's hand free. She bent to help the old woman to her feet.

85

'No,' Marna panted, 'do not touch me. Give me my staff.' Brand gave it to her and she struggled to her feet. 'Now, now I can do it. Now I can slay them. And myself. I have the maggot in me. Death is all I am good for. No, do not touch me.' But Breeze leaned quickly forward and kissed her on the cheek.

'Marna, Wildwood thanks you. The Woodlanders thank you.'

'Go. Leave me. Odo Cling comes.' She went to the edge of the Keystone and faced back along the Living Hill at the Halfmen running on the ridge. Brand and Breeze helped the children down off the boulder.

'Goodbye, Marna,' Susan cried.

'She cannot hear. She hears only her purpose.'

They ran back along the path to the abutment Already, on the other side of the Living Hill, Deathguards were on the slope. They ran sure-footedly on the narrow path. Their knives gleamed in their hands and their eyes showed like pink sockets under their hoods. They came so eagerly that one behind thrust a slower guard out of his way, and the man went tumbling down the hill, flopping like a bird, sending up puffs of dust as he clawed the earth. He bounced from sight over a boulder. The others made no sign; they came on silently. Marna, in her robe of pale blue, with her plait of hair pulled over her shoulder, stood on the Keystone with her staff in her hand.

'Odo Cling,' she cried.

But Cling stopped on the other side of the slope.

'Why doesn't he come?' Nick said.

'He holds the Bloodcat back,' Brand said. 'He wants to take Susan alive.'

The Cat strained on its leash. They saw its yellow eyes and milk-white fangs. It reared on its hind legs and they saw its claws gleaming in the sunlight. Muscles rippled under its red hide. Cling struck it with his whip. It cowered at his feet.

'If he released the Cat nothing could save us.'

'They're going to kill Marna,' Susan wept.

The first Deathguard had reached the Keystone. He climbed up the grass at its side, holding his knife in his teeth.

'Odo Cling, come!' Marna cried.

But Cling stayed back. Members of his Deathguard ran by him on to the hill. Out in the centre a dozen men had scrambled up the sides of the Keystone. Others ran silently on, making for the party on the abutment. The only sound was their padding feet.

'Now,' Breeze whispered, 'before it is too late.'

And Marna raised her staff. She faced back up the slope, she seemed to look into the sky. Deathguards came sliding out on to the jutting Keystone.

'Oh Living Hill, forgive me!' Marna cried. She brought the heel of her staff down with a sharp blow on the rock. The sound came cracking through the air. And everything was still. The clouds in the sky stood still, the breeze was still. The Deathguards froze in their movements. They stood as though made of stone. One of them cried out with fear; and the Bloodcat gave a dreadful howl.

'What's happening?' Susan whispered.

Breeze put her arm round her. 'Listen.'

From deep in the Living Hill came a small creaking sound, like the creaking of house-timbers on a still night.

'Marna struck the Keystone and the Living Hill begins to die.'

There came a groan, a sound of grief from deep within the earth. It began to grow, to rumble. It was the rumble of herds moving, of heavy trucks thundering along highways. It grew and grew. And as it grew the Living Hill began to shake. The Keystone reared from the earth, it rose with a slow majesty, thrusting huge and grey as a battleship. The Deathguards tumbled off and fell like twists of paper. But Marna stood on the prow, holding her staff. It was fused in the stone, and Marna was lifted up till she towered in the sky. Then the rock began to fall with a stately slowness. All about, the Living Hill was sliding into the forest. The Death-guards fluttered on the liquid earth and vanished beneath its surface. The Keystone crashed down, spraying stones like water. It began to tumble end over end. A single flash of blue: Marna was gone.

Far below a giant fan of earth spread into the forest. Dust smoked up. It seemed the forest was burning. And still from up the slope, from against the sky, the living earth of the hill roared down. The sound was like a hundred earthquakes. It seemed it would never stop. The abutment where the children stood was jumping like the lid of a boiling pot. It threw them off their feet. They clutched the rock and held on for their lives.

At last the shaking stopped and the air was still. Now and then came the small shiver of a sliding stone. Nick and Susan climbed to their feet. They looked at the huge wet wound in the land. The whole of the Living Hill was gone. All that was left was a deep V gouged in the mountain. It glistened brown and yellow. Its sides were slick as paint. It ran up out of sight, and down to the fan of earth that had crushed the forest.

Marna lay crushed in there. The Deathguards lay crushed. Only a dozen had scrambled back. They stood with Odo Cling, looking down like a band of tourists overawed by some great gorge or fall.

'They're dead,' Susan whispered. 'Everybody's dead.'

'Except for Odo Cling,' Nick said. 'And his Bloodcat.' He counted. 'Eleven men. But they can't get us.'

'Marna's dead.'

The Woodlanders had gathered in a group at the edge of the slip. They faced out to Wildwood. Breeze began to sing. One by one the others joined in. It was a dirge.

'That's for Marna,' Nick said.

'And the trees that died. And the Living Hill.'

Jimmy Jaspers had struggled out of his litter. He came to their side, bent painfully in two. 'There's too much bloddy singin' goes on here. They should get across an' throttle that little geezer.'

'There's no way across.'

'Yeah. She was some slip. I reckon nursey knew a trick or two.'

The song changed its rhythm. It became a hymn of gratitude and praise. Odo Cling shook his whip in the air. The Bloodcat raised its head and howled. But the Woodlanders sang on till their hymn was done.

Breeze and Brand came back to the children. 'Marna has saved us,' Breeze said. 'We have given thanks.'

'I wish there was a song I could sing too.'

Breeze touched her cheek. 'Your tears are thanks enough.'

Nick said, 'Odo Cling's still alive. Will he follow us?'

'Yes, he'll follow,' Brand said. 'He still has his Bloodcat and some men. But he cannot cross. He must go down to the forest and climb up on this side. By that time we will be over the pass. The Bloodcat comes from the hot lands. She will not follow in the snow.'

'So we've got away.'

Jimmy Jaspers straightened up. He raised his head and laughed. 'Hey Cling,' he yelled, 'I'll bet that landslide made yer wet yer pants. There's no way yer can catch us now so go home to yer mammy.'

7

Morninghall

Two days' marching brought them to the pass. Another day's
hard trudging in the snow and they came down into the hills
where the Birdfolk ran their flocks of half-wild goats. It was
a bitter country. Grass with blades as rough as emery paper
grew from the soil. Thorn trees, yellow-tipped and poisonous,
blocked the trails. In every hollow an icy stream foamed down.
The wind from off the mountains cut like a knife.

At nightfall they made a fire and warmed some food. They
slept huddled in blankets. In the morning the band broke in
two. The Woodlanders from Marna's hospital were going
south along the foothills. They would return to Wildwood
round the southern end of the range. Dale and Verna led them.
These two had been good friends to Susan. She felt lonely
to see them go. But Breeze and Brand were left. And Nick
was there. And bad old Jimmy Jaspers was on his feet, scratching himself, grumbling at the food.

'What I really needs is a bit o' meat. All this greens an'
stuff'll give me gas.'

'They're good for you, Jimmy. They'll make you strong.'

'That's what me old Mum used to say. God rest 'er. Then
she'd give me a belt on the lugs with the back of 'er 'and.
Aargh.' He scratched his bandages. 'These bloddy things is
itchin'. I'd be all right if I had me baccy.'

Brand came back from a scouting trip down the stream.
'It turns north. We will follow it.'

'How will we find the Birdfolk?' Nick asked.

'We won't do that,' Brand laughed. 'They'll find us.
They've found us already.' He pointed at the sky. It took
a lot of searching, but at last the children saw them: two tiny

spots turning in the blue. 'They've been there since we crossed the pass yesterday.'

'Why don't they come down?'

'They will when they're ready. In the meantime, we go on.'

They went on for two days. They followed the stream down the thorny hills and turned north along the foot of the mountains. Always the two dots were in the sky. They circled lazily. It made Susan nervous. But apart from that she was reasonably happy. Sometimes she fretted for home, and at others felt weak with fright at the thought of what she must do, but mostly she enjoyed being with Nick and Brand and Breeze – yes, and Jimmy Jaspers, though he never washed – and enjoyed this strange new world, the jagged hills, the roaring waterfalls, the yellow plains in the distance, and the agile goats skittering up the gullies. At night she lay wrapped in blankets and watched the stars. The Milky Way was there, but everything else was different: no Southern Cross, no Big Dipper, no Venus in the western sky and no red Mars. One of those stars out there might be her sun. That made her lonely and scared. She thought of Marna dying in the landslip, and of Freeman Wells lying with his neck broken at the foot of a cliff. Breeze and Brand were talking by the fire. Nick was sleeping quietly, his face red in the light. Jimmy Jaspers was snoring. Susan felt it was unfair that she had been chosen to save them. She wished the Mark had never been put on her. She wished she was safe in her bed, back on the farm.

On their third day of walking Jimmy Jaspers trapped a goat. They came on it suddenly, grazing by a stream. It was a young one and it made the mistake of running into a blind gully with sheer walls. Jimmy Jaspers was after it and had it by the hind legs before the others knew what he was up to. He dragged it out to a patch of grass by the stream and squatted on it.

'Now we'll have some meat.' He took his clasp-knife from his pocket and opened a blade.

'No,' Susan cried. She had seen sheep slaughtered on the farm, but there was food in their bags and no reason for the goat to die.

'Close yer eyes if yer don't like it,' Jimmy Jaspers said.

'Stop,' Brand said. 'Woodlanders do not eat any flesh.'

'That's why yer so skinny.'

'The Birdfolk own these goats. They will punish you.'

'There's no sich thing as Birdfolk. Them things up there is eagles.'

Nick looked into the sky. 'That's what you think,' he said.

There was a rushing of huge wings, a buffeting downward wind, and a brown shape fell into their circle and struck at Jimmy Jaspers with its legs and sent him rolling along the ground into the stream.

'Who steals the herds of Morninghall?' boomed a voice.

The being standing there, with one clawed foot resting on the goat, was neither bird nor man. Susan shrank from it – she could not tell what it was. She just knew that its green eyes were terrible. They were bird eyes in a human face.

Jimmy Jaspers rose spluttering from the water. He still held his knife. He came up the bank, yelling with rage. 'That's my goat, yer hairy stork. By gum, I'll pluck an' singe yer. I'll have yer on a plate for Christmas dinner.'

The Birdman had his giant wings outspread. He brought them smacking together with a sound like a gunshot. The blast of air sent Jimmy Jaspers reeling back into the stream. He rose again, but Breeze called, 'Look above you, Jimmy Jaspers.'

They all looked up. The second Birdman was floating overhead. His wings were so wide they blotted out the sun.

'He could lift you as high as the mountains and let you go. Then on the way down Jimmy you could wonder if a piece of meat was worth it.'

The Birdman holding the goat lifted his claw and the animal ran bleating into the rocks.

'Who comes into our land? Speak.'

Brand stepped forward. 'I am Brand of Wildwood. This is my mate, Breeze. The three we bring have travelled through the maze of Freeman Wells. We do not know their world. But one of them wears the Mark on her wrist.'

Slowly the Birdman folded his outspread wings. He looked at Susan with his green eyes. 'This one?' He stepped up to Susan, towering over her. His human face was suddenly like an eagle's. 'Show me.'

She rolled back her sleeve and held out her wrist. The Birdman looked. He called to his companion. 'Redwing.' She – something in her face said she was female – dropped lightly at his side. 'See.'

She looked at the Mark. 'Yes.' She unfolded a downy arm from the feathers on her breast and touched Susan's wrist. 'We must take her to Morninghall.'

'The Mark is true. Marna has examined it,' Breeze said.

'The Council must see. They are the guardians of the Half.'

'How far is Morninghall?'

'Another day at your groundling pace.'

'Do Halfmen follow us?'

'No. We have watched since you crossed the pass. Half a day behind you Halfmen came. Odo Cling was leading, with a Bloodcat. But the Cat would not mount into the snow. Cling whipped it but it would not move. So they turned back. We knew you must be important for Cling to follow so eagerly. We would have come to you sooner but we did not like the look of your friend in the stream.'

'I don't like the look of you much either.' Jimmy climbed dripping up the bank. 'This world's like a bloddy fancy dress party. But I'll tell yer what, Pretty Polly, I'll leave yer goats alone if yer'll lay me an egg.'

'Jimmy,' Breeze warned. But Redwing laughed.

93

'You shall have meat at Morninghall. One who jokes as you do cannot be evil.'

The other Birdman gave his feathers a ruffle. 'I do not know whether we should trust him.'

'Jimmy's all right,' Susan said. 'He's helping us now.'

'You wear the Mark. We shall take your word. I am Wanderer. I am First Warrior of Morninghall. Redwing is my mate. She likes to laugh. But do not let your friend be cheeky to her.'

'You hear that, Jimmy?'

'Yerss. Flap yer wings cocky, an' dry me out a bit.'

They went on through the foothills for the rest of the day. Redwing and Wanderer flew overhead, lower than they had been in the morning. Now and then Redwing glided down to show them an easier path. Once she brought a large green fruit, harder than a pumpkin. She dropped it on a boulder and it split in two, exposing yellow flesh sweet as cherries. Even Jimmy Jaspers said it was good.

Wanderer found them a place to camp in a hollow out of the wind. As they crouched about the fire, warming their food, Redwing flew in. She carried a leather bag. 'There, featherless one.' She thrust it at Jimmy. 'I flew to Morninghall. Your jokes have earned you dinner.'

In the bag were dried strips of meat and a pan for frying it.

'And here,' Redwing said. She took a large blue egg from under each armpit and gave them to Jimmy. 'Specially laid.'

Jimmy's mouth dropped open. 'Yer didn'?'

Redwing pealed with laughter. 'Ah no, no. They are the eggs of the Bounder bird. I found a nest as I was flying back.'

So Jimmy Jaspers ate goat's meat bacon and fried eggs. He gave some to Nick. Though her mouth watered, Susan would not touch any. She felt a loyalty to Brand and Breeze. They sat about the fire and Brand told their tale to the Birdfolk, and Nick and Susan told what had happened in their world.

They made Jimmy Jaspers' part sound less wicked than it had been. Wanderer and Redwing stood on the other side of the fire. They could not sit, but rested on their legs and the tips of their wings. Nick guessed they were nearly three metres tall. Their wings, spread out, must cover seven metres. Although their feet were clawed and their bodies covered with feathers and down, they seemed more human than bird-like. He wondered if they were birds that had evolved from humans or the other way round. But when they took off with a great leap into the air – well away from the fire so the storm of wind would not scatter it – he decided that in spite of their human faces and human speech he must think of them as birds; the most magnificent birds he had ever seen. The last bright rays of the sun made a gleam of many colours on their wings as they beat powerfully away to the north.

Next morning the wind had died down. After an hour's walking they came to the Yellow Plains and followed a slow river along their western edge. Half a dozen Birdfolk were in the sky. Now and then they dropped down for a closer look at Susan. She became a little grumpy at the way the wind from their wings tangled her hair.

By mid-morning the ground was rising again. They climbed towards a rocky hill that stood like a footstool in front of the mountains. More and more Birdfolk appeared in the sky. They flew in from the north and east, or came swooping down from high in the mountains. Some carried goats in harnesses slung beneath them. Cries of welcome and the bleating of frightened animals filled the air.

'There will be a great feast to welcome you,' Brand said.

They climbed a grassy hill and as they reached the top Wanderer and Redwing dropped down at their sides. 'Here is Morninghall. Welcome, Susan Ferris. And welcome to your friends. No human, mixed or half man, has come here before, except Freeman Wells, and perhaps no human will come again.'

There was a hollow like a crater in the hill. It ran back smoothly to the cliffs of the footstool. There an opening large as a cathedral led into the mountain. Birdfolk were flying in and out. The mouth of the vast hall was lit by the sun, but further back lamps glowed on the walls and smaller openings led even deeper into the hill. Closer, in the hollow, fires burned. The smell of roasting goat meat drifted up. Birdfolk tended the fires, turning carcases on spits. Some flew in with loads of firewood. Others carried cooked food on iron platters up into the mouth of the hall and placed it on high tables set up there.

'Come,' Redwing said, 'the Council is waiting. The feast is ready to start.'

They went down the hollow among the fires. Everywhere Birdfolk called greetings and came forward to look at Susan more closely. At first she was pleased and excited, but by the time they reached the hall she was feeling oppressed. It was their tallness, she felt, the way they towered over her and fluffed their feathers out as a sign of respect. It made them seem fat and overfed. Yet she saw they were light, almost stringy, under their feathers. Their legs were long, with down extending to the claw. Most of their weight was in the upper body, in the muscles round their shoulders and chest, where the driving strength for their great wings was stored.

Wanderer and Redwing guided them into the hall. There a group of Birdfolk stood apart, watching them come up. 'Here is our Council,' Wanderer said. 'And this is Wise One. It was she who welcomed Freeman Wells.'

A tall grey-feathered Birdwoman stepped out from the group. 'I welcome you, Susan Ferris, and your friends. Wanderer and Redwing have seen the Mark. The Council would see it too. But I can see you are tired, and perhaps a little deafened by the welcome of our folk. Redwing will take you to a quiet place where you can rest. Return when you are ready. Do not hurry. We have waited twelve turns for your coming. We can wait a little longer.'

This kindness made Susan feel like crying. How had Wise One known that to be alone for a while was what she wanted more than anything? She did not even want Nick. Redwing led her deep into the hall. Then she branched off into a side hall, and from that into a long bright tunnel leading into the hill.

'Redwing?'

'Yes, Susan?'

'What I'd like is a bath. And somewhere to wash my clothes. They're filthy.'

'That is where I am taking you.' She pushed aside a feathered drape and they entered a room. 'This is where Wanderer and I live.' A window opened on to a view of the plain and river. Susan went to it and looked out. The mountain chain ran northward. In the east, beyond the plain, other mountains rose, with a dark forest on their foothills.

'It's beautiful. It's a lovely land.'

'Worth saving, Susan?'

'Yes.'

'The burden is very great for one so young.'

'I can do it.'

'Yes, I see you can. Freeman Wells chose wisely.'

'He didn't have any choice.'

'Perhaps some greater being made it then. But careful child, do not fall out. You don't have any wings.' She drew Susan back from the window and led her across the room. 'Here is the bath. There are hot springs in the mountain. It is not deep, see.' The bath was in a wide hollow in the floor. Redwing stepped in, fluffed her feathers out, half opened her wings, and splashed water everywhere. Susan almost giggled. She was like a giant parakeet in a giant birdbath. She stepped out, shook herself dry, and said, 'That is better. Stay in as long as you like, Susan. I have made a human bed in the other room if you want to sleep.' Susan watched as she went into the main room, stepped on to the windowsill, launched herself, and glided out of sight round the mountain.

She washed her clothes in the bath. Her shorts and shirt were filthy and her Woodlander cloak stained with berry juice and dust. Water ran into and out of the bath continuously. When it was clean again, she lowered herself in and lay there with steaming water lapping her chin. There was no soap but that did not seem to matter. She felt all the dust and grime, all the ache and tiredness of her journey soaking out of her. She almost went to sleep in the bath.

Later she slept on the bed Redwing had made. When she woke Redwing was watching her.

'What time is it? Are they waiting for me?'

'Yes,' Redwing said. 'The feasting is done. I have brought you food. Then I will take you to them.'

'Where are my clothes?'

'Brightfeather is drying them. She is one of my brood.'

Susan looked out the window. A young golden Birdgirl was looping and diving in the sky, with Susan's clothes trailing on a string behind her. Susan laughed. 'You think of everything.' She ate her platter of food. Then Redwing called Brightfeather and the Birdgirl swooped down and landed neatly on the windowsill. 'Greetings, Susan Ferris. I dropped one of your socks but I managed to catch it.'

'Thank you,' Susan said. She unwrapped herself from the bed coverings and dressed. 'Oh I wish I had a brush, my hair's all tangled.'

'A brush?' Redwing said. 'Brightfeather.' The Birdgirl launched herself and flew away. A moment later she was back with a beautiful brush, its back inlaid with coloured stones. She handed it to Susan. 'I use it for my pet goat. But you can keep it.'

'No —' Susan began; but Redwing said, 'All the Birdfolk would like to give you something, but we know you cannot burden yourself, you have far to go. So take this one thing from my daughter. It shall stand for all we cannot give you.'

'Well,' Susan said. The brush ran like water through her hair. 'Thank you. I'll keep it all my life.'

When she was ready Redwing led her back along the passage to the great hall and down to the entrance. Wise One came to meet her. 'Welcome again, Susan Ferris. You have bathed and slept? And eaten too? I see your eyes are brighter. That is good. Your cousin Nick has told us your story. You have come through many dangers. Morninghall will praise you in its songs.'

'I haven't done anything yet,' Susan said. 'The hardest part is coming.'

'That is so. But you will succeed.' Her green eyes burned. Susan began to feel oppressed again, and thought that Wise One wasn't very wise. She had liked her better when she was being kind.

'Do you want to see the Mark?'

'Yes, child. I saw it on Freeman Wells, in this very hall. I would count it an honour to see that sign again.' She called the Council to her. They came, stately and slow, tall Birdmen and Birdwomen, with their feathers a little ragged from a lifetime of flying. Susan felt small standing amongst them. She rolled up her sleeve. 'There you are.' They bent close. She heard their soft exclamations and felt their breath on her arm. Nick was a little way off. He winked at her.

'It is the Mark.'

'The true Mark.'

'She is the Bearer.'

'There was never any doubt,' Wise One said. 'Cover your arm, Susan. We will trouble you no more.' She walked to the entrance of the hall and signalled a young Birdman standing there. The young one raised a horn and blew a long silver blast. At once the folk outside were still. Those flying dropped quickly down. Silence filled the crater.

'Come and stand with me, Susan,' Wise One said. Susan went to her side. Wise One spread her wings and Susan felt the comfort of a wall of feathers at her back.

'Folk of Morninghall,' Wise One cried. 'I speak for the Council of the Hall. I speak for all Birdfolk. See this human child. She is Susan Ferris. She has come from another world, through many perils. Halfmen have pursued her. She has escaped a Bloodcat. She has fled the Evil Doer, Odo Cling, and come to us. She comes in the footsteps of Freeman Wells – that Freeman Wells who lives forever in our Song. This child wears the Mark of Freeman Wells. He it was who placed the Mark on her. She is his Chosen One. And now she comes to claim from us the Half that rests inside Mount Morningstar. Birdfolk, praise her. Morninghall, give her your strength. For she must journey far, to face that Dark on Darkness, Otis Claw. Give, I say!'

At once the Birdfolk roared. They sprang into the air. Their wings beat like the sea on shingle beaches. A huge wind burst inside the crater like a bomb, scattering fire and wood, throwing rocks about like hailstones. The Birdfolk rose into the air in a great multi-coloured shield. They blotted out the sun.

Susan cowered back in Wise One's wing. 'Do not be afraid,' Wise One cried. 'They make a gift to you.'

She felt as if she were on the bottom of the sea, watching a giant stingray float overhead.

'Fly Morninghall,' Wise One cried. The shield of Birdfolk wheeled away. It mounted, undulating, into the sky, and climbed towards the sun. Redwing was gone with it, Wanderer too. Only the old ones of the Council remained, and those too young to fly.

'Where are they going?' Susan whispered.

The shield grew smaller and smaller, until it was no larger in the sky than a black old-fashioned penny.

'They go to ask blessing from the sun. That strength and blessing they will bring to you.'

Susan watched until the black spot in the sky merged with the sun. Then for a long while nothing happened. From mountain-chain to mountain the sky was empty. 'When will they come back?'

'They are coming now.'

She could not see. The sun burned her eyes.

'There,' Nick cried, pointing. She saw something tumbling from the sky. It fell fast and straight as a stone.

'He'll be killed,' Susan cried.

Down, down, the tumbling Birdman came. She saw that he would smash into the crater. But at the last moment, when he was below the rim, his wings snapped out. There was a creaking of bones, a shrieking of air. The Birdman swooped along the crater floor, dust puffed up like a smoke-trail in his wake. But the Birdman gave a flick, he braked himself, climbed in a sudden sickening swoop until he was poised over her head, and dropped with astonishing gentleness at her feet. She looked at him. He towered over her. He seemed to glow with the warmth of the sun, his green eyes shone like suns. She felt them burning into her head. He reached an arm across his body, plucked a feather from his half-folded wing, and laid it at her feet. Then he turned and strode away and took his place on the crater rim.

'Here comes the next one,' Nick said.

All through the afternoon they fell, and swooped across the crater, and laid their feathers at her feet. It was a display of superb skill and strength. But it was more. Susan felt herself choking with emotion. The wind of their coming dashed her hair across her eyes, but she pushed it away, and tried to look each one in the eyes. The pile of feathers mounted at her feet. She felt herself growing taller, stronger.

'Seven hundred and ten so far,' Nick said.

Redwing came. She smiled as she plucked her feather. Susan saw a drop of blood glistening on its stem. Then the giant warriors fell from the sky. The crater seemed to boom as their wings snapped open. They made great groans of pain. Wanderer came last. He fell, and swooped, and stood in the air over her, and dropped gently as a leaf from a tree. He laid his feather at her feet.

'Morninghall has praised you.' He strode away to his place.

Susan turned slowly to Wise One. 'Can I take a feather?'

'We would be honoured, Susan.'

She stepped forward and reached into the pile. She did not choose, but let her hand come down where it would. She grasped the feather by the stem and lifted it in front of her. It was a deep blue one, streaked with red. She looked at the Birdfolk ranged about the crater rim. The dying sun had brought out all their colours and made their eyes flash like emeralds. She held the feather high. She did not know what she was going to say, but heard her voice rise into the air as sharp and strong as a trumpet call. 'I thank you, Morninghall. I have taken your strength. I shall carry it with me into the Darkness, and try to use it well.'

Then she turned and ran. She ran past Nick and Brand and Breeze and through the Council. Behind her a sound like thunder rose. The Birdfolk were clapping their great wings. She ran across the hall and down the passage and came to Redwing's room. She threw herself on the bed and lay there sobbing, with the red and blue feather hugged to her breast.

Later Nick came in. 'That was a good speech.'

'Were they offended when I ran away?'

'They understood. Wise One says she's taking you to get the Half in the morning.'

'Where?'

'Mount Morningstar. I wish I could come too.'

'I wish I could stay here. Stay forever.'

'I don't. Imagine living with Birdfolk and not being able to fly.'

'Yes, I suppose you're right. Where's Jimmy Jaspers?'

Nick gave a snort. 'He ate himself silly. Then he found

out they've got a forge here, where they work iron. So he took off there. He's been gone all afternoon. Says there's something he wants to make.'

Redwing came in. She brought food and drink, and stayed with Susan, telling her tales and legends of the Birdfolk until the sun was down and the room was dark. Then Susan slept. She woke in the morning to the call of the silver horn, and bathed quickly and plaited her hair. She ate the food Redwing brought, then walked with a feeling between elation and fear down to the entrance of the hall.

'Wanderer will carry you,' Wise One said. 'It was he who carried Freeman Wells. And I will fly at your side, though I think it will do my joints no good.' She stretched her old wings painfully. 'Rheumatism.'

Two Birdmen brought the chair Susan would ride in. It was, she thought, rather like a shopping-basket, with handles standing high. Wanderer would grasp those and carry her like groceries. She wriggled inside. It was lined with down. 'You will need it,' Redwing said. 'Mount Morningstar is cold.'

Nick grinned ruefully. 'You can't smuggle me in?' Brand and Breeze spoke encouragingly. However it was not the flight that frightened Susan, but the thought of the Half. Soon she would see it, and claim it. What was it like?

Wise One said, 'I must launch myself from a window. The days when I could leap into flight are gone.' She went back into the hall, and a few moments later came gliding round the curve of the hill. 'Come Susan,' she called, 'come Wanderer. We have far to go.'

Wanderer touched wings with Redwing. He took two steps and beat up into the air. Then he came gliding back and grasped the handles of Susan's chair and swung it up easily beneath him.

'Good-bye, Susan,' Nick called.

Wanderer climbed in long sweeps. The hills began to stretch and the plains to spread themselves out. Soon Susan felt her ears go pop. She wondered how high they were going. Wise One was far below, tiny as a sparrow. The crater was a dent scooped by a teaspoon, and Morninghall a shrunken old potato. She looked up and saw Wanderer's breast feathers rippling in the sun. His wings beat heavily and his feathers crackled like paper. An icy wind was rushing about her face. She pulled the hood of her Woodlander cloak tight about her ears and snuggled deep in the downy chair. They must be as high, she thought, as the Morninghall Birdfolk had climbed the previous day.

Wanderer stopped at last and floated on his wings. 'Susan,' he called, 'you can see the whole of our land now. The plains run northward for three days' flight. All between the mountain ranges is Morninghall land. Eastward you see Mount Morningstar. Beyond are lands belonging to other Halls. We live in peace with them.'

'Where do the Bloodcats live?'

'Northward. Far to the north, in the hotlands. They do not come this far unless Halfmen bring them.' He wheeled round. 'There is Darkland, with the ocean beyond. You cannot see it for the evil smoke. Where Wildwood ends, that jagged line is Sheercliff. The smoke reaches up. Soon it will swallow the forest. It will come leaking round the ends of the mountains into the plains of Morninghall.'

Susan looked at this lovely land, spread out like a rumpled quilt in the sun. She could not believe she was the one who could save it.

'Wanderer?' she said.

'Yes. You wonder why we do not fight. We who are so strong and pleased with ourselves. Why do we not fly down to Darkland and drop a boulder on Otis Claw and squash him like a maggot? But Susan, there is a law, a dispensation. Some say that in the ancient days the Gods sat on Mount Morningstar and portioned out the world among their creatures. Manhome to Humankind. Wildwood to the Wood–

landers. The upland and the mountains to the Birdfolk. And sea and underground to other folk. That is the tale. I leave it to the wise ones who study such things, though I love to hear the legend told in song. But this I know – westward of the mountains we cannot fly. There was some ancient wrong, and we are punished, we are locked in our land. Even so, we try. We sent an army out to crush Otis Claw. That was in the time of Freeman Wells. And many a young birdman has started out alone, thinking to win glory for himself. But none come back. And the army perished. Westward of the mountains a dreadful weariness comes down on all Birdfolk. Our wings fold up, we tumble to the ground and are dashed to pieces. My son, my only son, this last turn ...' He gave a groan and was silent.

'I'm sorry,' Susan began, but Wanderer cut her off. 'So, we turn aside from a task that should be ours and leave it to a weak stranger from another world.'

'I'm not so weak,' Susan said. 'You gave me your strength.'

'Yes, yes, you have that. There is nothing else we can offer.' He floated silently.

After a while Susan said, 'Which is Mount Morningstar?'

'The central peak. The highest one.'

She had thought that must be it – a mountain standing up like a sword in the sky.

'In olden times, when Birdfolk robbed and killed, there was a famous brigand called Redclaw. He kept his treasure in a cave on the north face of the mountain. It was abandoned centuries ago. None go there. It is known only to Wise One and to me. There we took Freeman Wells. There he left the Half. No living thing has gone in that cave since.'

Wise One came labouring up. They heard her old wings creaking. She took her place beside Wanderer. 'I have not flown so hard in many turns.'

'From here it is all down air. I have told her of the cave.'

'Then let us go. I shall pretend I am young again.' She

banked and started off. Wanderer followed. Then for an hour they raced down the frozen air. Susan huddled in her nest and watched Mount Morningstar grow until it filled the sky. Its west side was unlit, but when the Birdfolk circled to the north she saw huge glaciers and banks of ice shining in the sun. Wise One tilted her wings and sped down like a hawk and Wanderer followed. Below the snowline a black cliff dropped sheer into the forest. A ledge like a hand jutted from its side. Wise One made for it. For the first time on their long flight from the west she flapped her wings. She passed the ledge – it was, Susan saw, about the size of the roof of a haybarn – and looped back to it steeply, and came down in the centre, neat as a parachutist. She folded her wings. Wanderer came in beside her and hovered a moment to let Susan out of the chair. She scrambled free and stood shivering on the sun-warmed rock.

'This is Redclaw's Hall. There is the door,' Wise One said.

Susan looked at the egg-shaped opening in the cliff. The sun slanted in, lighting the threshold of a room. It seemed almost welcoming. At her back was only space, the long dizzy drop down to the forest.

'Do I go in alone?'

'We will follow.'

She tried not to be nervous. After all, it was the good Half in there. She went to the door and stepped inside. It was a hall large enough for a score of Birdfolk. High in the front wall apertures were cut and bars of sunlight ran into the gloom. There was nothing inside – nothing, not even dust. She wondered where all the treasure had gone, and tried to imagine pirate Birdfolk living in this place, and setting off on raids into the plains.

'Where's the Half?'

Wise One and Wanderer had entered behind her. 'There, at the back,' Wise One said.

A narrow shelf was cut in the wall. She went slowly towards

it. Freeman Wells had come here, now she came. She began to tremble. She put out her hand and drew it back. Lying on the shelf, as though it were some bit of rubbish left in an old empty house, was a piece of amber-coloured glass, shaped like a teardrop.

'Is that it?' But she knew. She reached out, and felt her hand begin to travel of its own accord.

With her fingers steady, she picked up the Half.

8

Underhand Chop

Nick went up to the crater rim with the young Birdfolk and watched them practise flying. They spread their wings and glided into the hollow. Now and then one would try a cautious flap, but this usually led to a tumble on landing. They got rather bad-tempered. Nick wandered away. If he had to live here, he thought, he would build himself a hang-glider and show them they weren't the only ones who could fly.

Jimmy Jaspers came out of the hall. He climbed the rim and set off towards the river. Nick wondered what he was up to. He ran to catch up. Jimmy moved along quickly, hopping like a goat from rock to rock. He bellowed a song about a girl who had loved a sailor and been left in the lurch. When Nick caught up he had stopped at a thicket of thorn trees.

'What do yer reckon, younker? Reckon I'll find a good straight one in there?'

'What for?' Nick asked.

'A handle fer me axe.' He showed Nick an axe head. 'Cast and tempered 'er yestiddy. Sharpened 'er this mornin'. Feel that edge. Go easy, yer'll 'ave yer finger orf.' He rolled up his sleeve and shaved some hairs off his arm. 'When I catches up with Odo Cling I'll slice 'im up fer bacon.'

He took out his clasp knife and hacked down one of the thorn trees and trimmed off its branches. 'I reckon this'll do. She's good tough wood.'

Nick sat with him on a rock while he shaped and smoothed a handle. The old man spat on his hands. He worked easily and fast. His knife was chisel, plane and sand-paper. By lunch-time the axe handle was ready. He fitted it to the axe head and hammered in a wedge with a piece of rock. He whirled it round his head. 'I reckon she's right. You ain't seen me use an axe, 'ave yer younker? I won the underhand chop six years runnin' at the Fells Bush A and P show. Let's get up there an' cut them pretty pollies a bit o' firewood.'

He worked all afternoon in the crater. Birdfolk flew in with logs to keep him supplied. By sundown he had a stack as high as his head.

'I reckon I'm in trim. Bring on yer Odo Cling.'

A Birdman landed with a flurry of wings. 'They are coming. Wise One and Wanderer and Susan.'

Nick peered into the east, where the distant mountains stood out in the dying sun. In a moment he saw two dots moving on the pink and yellow sky. He felt as if he were in an airport, waiting for a plane to come in from Australia. Then the strangeness of things rushed in on him and he almost cried out with disbelief. This was Morninghall, on the planet O. Those dots were Birdfolk. Susan was flying home with the Half, coming to save the world. He grasped Jimmy Jaspers by the arm.

'Easy, son,' the old man said. 'Yer gotter roll with the punches.'

Wise One came down in a flat glide and landed by the entrance of the hall. Wanderer dropped more steeply and put Susan's chair down light as a cushion. Susan climbed out. Her cheeks were flushed with cold and she looked tired.

Wise One faced the crater. She spread her wings, though they shook with weariness. 'Morninghall,' she cried, 'your guardianship is over. Susan Ferris has claimed the Half.'

The Birdfolk clapped their wings, softly, gravely. They seemed a little sad.

Nick ran up to the entrance. Brand and Breeze came running. The Council gathered round. Nick gave Susan a hug.

'Can I see?'

But she shook her head. She had her fist shut tightly. Her knuckles were white. 'No, no, I can't show anyone.'

'Why?'

'Because . . . because . . .'

'Leave her,' Redwing said; and Breeze, peering at her anxiously, said, 'Do not trouble her now. She needs to rest.'

The Birdwoman and the Woodlander led her away.

Nick moped about. He felt left out of things. He sat with Brand and Jimmy by a fire and ate his meal. He worried about Susan. What would happen if she got sick?

Later in the evening Breeze knelt beside him. 'Susan would like to see you.'

'What happened? Is she all right?'

'She will tell you. Do not keep her talking.'

Nick went back through the hall, along the passage, and into Redwing's room. It was lit with flames burning in pans of oil. Susan was lying on the bed, with coverings up to her chin. The light was dull, but he saw the flush was gone from her cheeks. She smiled at him.

'I'm sorry, Nick. I'm not usually like this.'

'What happened?'

'They took me to a cave on the mountain. It was high up, like – like a kingfisher's nest in a bank. No one had been there since Freeman Wells. I got the Half.'

'Can I see?'

'It was lying on a shelf at the back of the cave. Just lying there. I picked it up. And Nick – I thought I was – I thought I was going to break into little pieces. Something went right through me. It was like electricity. I felt every part of me – my heart and my muscles and bones. My eyeballs and teeth and toenails. It was horrible. They all separated. And then, somehow, they all came back together. But I felt I was different. I was changed. Something was added to me. Does that make sense?'

'No.'

'You have to feel it yourself. I'm the only one who can ever feel it. I suppose the Half was just saying – saying it knew me.'

'Is that why you won't show it to anyone?'

'Yes. It's too important. Nick, it's light as a wishbone. But when I picked it up it felt like lead. I felt I was picking up half of everybody in the world. I wouldn't even show Red-wing or Breeze. It's not like a new bangle or hairclip – everybody going Ooh! and Aah!'

'They wouldn't do that.'

'I know. I can't be fair. But I'll show it to you. You're the only one.'

She drew her fist out from the coverings. She held it out to him and opened it. The Half lay on her palm. Nick looked at it and pulled a face. 'It doesn't look much.' Like Wool-worth's plastic jewellery, he thought, or something made of perspex and polished up. Its shape was interesting: a teardrop, curved like a moon. He saw how the other Half would fit into it and make a circle. And its colour was rather nice – like weak lemon tea. There was a tiny spot in it like a tea-leaf, dark red, almost black.

'Have you put it on your birthmark? Is it alive?'

'No. I'm frightened it would take all the good out of me. I'm going to wait till I've got them both. Till I'm at the Motherstone.'

'If you get there.'

'I will. I know it now.'

She closed her fist and pushed it under the blankets. 'I'm tired. I want to go to sleep. Good-night, Nick.'

He sat by the fire with Brand and Breeze and Jimmy, listening to the Birdfolk sing tales of their ancestors. He felt he would be happy to stay here forever; then knew that he could never belong. This was the last night he would spend with the Birdfolk. He wondered if, years from now, his name and Susan's and Jimmy Jaspers' would be remembered in Morninghall. Perhaps there would be a song – The Quest of Susan Ferris and Nicholas Quinn. He liked the sound of that.

In the morning their little band gathered in the entrance of the hall. Nobody made speeches. One by one the Council members folded Susan in their wings. Redwing gave her a belt made of beaten goathide. She had stayed up into the night making it, working Birdfolk motifs along its length and colouring them with dye. Two small pouches were fixed on it, one on each side of the buckle.

'For the Halves, Susan.'

Susan belted it round her waist, under her cloak. She put the Half in the right-hand pouch. Nick glimpsed its amber gleam.

'Carry our strength in your heart,' Wise One said.

The Birdfolk of Morninghall rose in the air. This time they made no shield, but flew informally, swooping and weaving casually in the air. All through the morning they followed the band down the Yellow Plains and along the river. Then, one by one, they dropped away, and flew back to Morninghall or the mountains. Soon only Redwing and Wanderer were left, and five young Birdfolk who carried the packs. Jimmy Jaspers would not give up his axe. Apart from that they travelled light, and made good time. At nightfall the Birdfolk came dropping out of the sky and laid the gear in a camping-place Wanderer had chosen. Nick and Susan slept deeply after their day's march.

At the end of the second day they were opposite the pass. Nick did not look forward to crossing the snow.

'Won't Odo Cling have some guards there?'

'Yes,' Brand said, 'a company of guards. They are down below the snowline on the other side. Wanderer flew high and spotted them.'

'They'll stop us going over,' Nick said.

'We're not going that way. And we're not going round the end of the range. There are guards there too.'

'Where, then?'

'Wanderer knows a secret trail. It lies a day's march south.

He does not know what lies on the other side, but it must come out somewhere in Wildwood. Once there we are safe. We can find the Stonefolk.'

Susan drew her blanket round herself. 'Where's the Blood-cat?'

'Wanderer does not know. He has not seen the Cat. Or Odo Cling.'

'Cling?' Jimmy Jaspers said. ''E's mine. You leave Cling ter me.'

Next day they followed a river on the plains. The mountains rose sheer on their right, with rocky cliffs and giant slides of shingle. Streams ran out of gorges or tumbled down in summer waterfalls. In the afternoon they began to climb. The way was broken, barred by streams and boulders. Redwing flew low over them, pointing out the easier paths. They came on to a plateau grown over with mountain grass and thorn trees. On the other side the mountain wall made an unbroken line. They trudged towards it, and got there by nightfall, scratched and weary. Wanderer and the young Birdfolk had made a fire. They had food cooking and hot drinks steaming in mugs. That night they did not fly back to Morninghall, but slept about the campfire, standing balanced on their wing-tips. Nick lay in his blankets watching them. They were like tall statues made of wood, like guardian angels. It made him cold to think that tomorrow they would fly away for ever.

In the morning Wanderer flew into the mountains, climbing steadily where the wall was less steep. Redwing watched him anxiously. The morning sun gleamed on his wings. 'He goes too far. He is near the mark of forbidding. Ah, ah, no!'

Wanderer seemed to stagger in his flight. But he managed to turn. With his wings half-closed he made a lumpy glide back down to them. He skidded on the ground and tumbled over. Redwing rushed to him and covered him with her wings. He lay groaning for a moment. 'I went too close. It took my wings like a cramp.' He managed to climb to his feet. 'The way is open. I could see no further. But it is clear to the top. What lies beyond I cannot say.' He looked at Brand. 'It is a hard way. You must have care. I shall show you where it begins.'

'No,' Redwing said.

'Yes. If we can ask this child, Susan Ferris, to go into the Darkland and face Otis Claw, then I can carry Brand awhile, even though my wings are tearing off.'

He launched himself and hovered over Brand. Brand took hold of his legs. 'He is lighter than Susan Ferris,' Wanderer joked. He rose laboriously into the air, and flapped away to the mountains, with Brand clinging beneath. They circled there, climbing and gliding, for several minutes. Two of the young Birdfolk flew close, keeping an anxious watch on them.

'Everyone gets a ride but me,' Nick grumbled.

Wanderer and Brand came back and landed. 'It is a hard way,' Brand said. 'But the only way. We must start at once and be at the top by nightfall. I do not want to spend more than one night on the mountains.'

The young Birdfolk flew the packs as far up the trail as they could go. Then they hovered over the party, making their farewells, and flew away north.

'We must go now,' Redwing said. 'Remember us, Susan Ferris. We will remember you.' She embraced her in her wings. She embraced Nick and Brand and Breeze. 'Them feathers'll make me sneeze,' Jimmy Jaspers protested. But he could not escape.

'Keep your axe sharp, Jimmy,' Wanderer said.

Then he too embraced Susan. 'Go well,' he said simply. He kissed her on the brow. Then he went to the edge of the camp, sprang into the air, and beat away north. Redwing ran, and jumped, and followed him. 'Goodbye,' she called in a long fading cry.

Nick and Susan watched until they vanished in the sky. 'We'll never see them again,' Nick said.

'No,' Susan said. She felt inside her cloak, inside her T-shirt, and drew out the feather streaked with red. All morning as they climbed she held it in her hand.

Brand led them up a gorge slanting into the mountains. It climbed in a series of broken steps. A stream of thawed snow-water ran down darkly in the shadows. Several times they had to wade through it. Their legs grew cold as ice. When the gorge opened out thorn trees blocked it. Jimmy Jaspers cleared the way with his axe. Towards midday they came to the place where the Birdfolk had left their packs. Climbing was harder after that. At midday Brand made a fire of thorn branches and heated food in a pan. He handed Susan a drink of warmed goat's milk.

'Do you think you can keep going?'

'I'm all right. Will we get to the top tonight?'

'With luck. How are you, Nick?'

'Fitter than I've ever been,' Nick groaned.

The gorge went on, narrow as a hallway. Its slanting sides blocked out the sun. Once Brand had to haul them up the side of a waterfall, using his rope. The rocks were slippery with ice. Lips of snow jutted out above them.

'An hour till sundown,' Brand said. He sounded anxious. But soon the floor of the gorge levelled out. The water lay in still pools, filmed with ice. They travelled miles it seemed on a kind of switchback, scrambling up, stumbling down. The shade began to thicken. Then Brand made a clicking sound with his tongue. 'Do you notice anything?'

Nick looked about. The water at his feet was moving again. 'The stream's running the opposite way. We must be going down.'

'We're over the top,' Brand said. 'This gorge runs like a cut through the middle of the range. Tomorrow you'll see Wildwood.'

Jimmy Jaspers had packed wood for a fire. They warmed food and dried their shoes, and slept curled in their blankets, shivering in the frozen air.

'I've knowed worse,' Jimmy said. 'I've 'ad me clothes froze so stiff I was like a knight in bloddy armour.'

In the morning Brand found a way to the top of the gorge. He led them up one by one. And there was Wildwood, sombre green in its morning shade. It ran so tightly up under the mountains it seemed they would be able to take two steps through the snow and float down into it.

'I know where we are,' Brand said. 'The stream runs down to the Mirror Cliffs. By midday we will find the Lizard Path. Tonight we will sleep in Wildwood. Wanderer's path has saved us many days.'

The gorge fell steeply to a plateau covered with bush. They went down easily, and turned away as the stream flowed south. 'We will see it again where it falls down the Mirror Cliffs. We call it Mountain's Grief. But we must take a quicker way. There is a cleft that will take us down to the path.'

He led them through the forest. Breeze kept darting off to pick leaves and berries, and brought them back for Nick and Susan to taste. Jimmy Jaspers would have nothing to do with them. His pack was stuffed with dried meat. The land dropped sharply into the cleft. They clambered down through mossy rocks and tall fern trees and came out on the Lizard Path, half-way between the plateau and Wildwood. The Mirror Cliffs stretched away to the north and south. They were smooth as ice and they folded in soft curves like a sheet of paper set on edge. Here and there tongues of bush ran down and licked the path.

'Sheercliff is taller, but these are just as steep. The path will take us to the southern end. You must walk carefully. Even Woodlanders have been known to fall.'

They ate lunch at the foot of the cleft. Then Susan lay back to rest. The sun was overhead. She felt warm for the first time in two days. For a moment or two she drifted off to sleep. Fragments of dream passed through her mind: dreams of warmth, of beds and fires and feathers. She smiled and murmured happily. Then she was flying high up by the sun, cosy in her nest; and then came swooping down close to the ground, over the Yellow Plains, over the tops of trees – and she came to a cave and circled close to its mouth, which drew her like a magnet, the way the yellow smoke had drawn her into the mineshaft. The pressure on her head was terrible. Suddenly the Bloodcat leapt out, screaming.

Susan woke with a cry. She sat up, looking wildly about.

'Susan,' Breeze cried, 'what is it? What's the matter?'

'I heard the Bloodcat.'

'You were dreaming, child.'

'No, no, I heard it. There! That's it again. The Bloodcat's coming.'

'I didn't hear anything,' Nick said.

Brand had moved out on to the path. 'Quiet,' he said. They were all still. They held their breath. The silence was like iron. Moment after moment it went on. Then Brand knelt on the path. 'Breeze.' She went to his side and looked where he was pointing. 'Yes,' she said, 'they have been this way.'

'Come,' Brand called. 'We must leave at once.'

'What is it?' Nick said.

'Halfmen have been this way.'

'With the Bloodcat. I can smell its scent,' Breeze said.

'They have been patrolling the Lizard Path. Odo Cling must have guessed we would come this way. Their spoor leads north. We will go south.'

'I heard the Bloodcat,' Susan said.

'No, child. That was in your mind. You were dreaming.'

'She weren't,' Jimmy Jaspers said. 'I can see the bloddy thing.'

They looked where he was pointing. The Mirror Cliffs had turned dull silver in the sun. The path ran along it like a thread, dividing it neatly in two. Three folds of the cliff away, black figures were moving on the thread. They were shapeless as inkblots in their cloaks. Except for Odo Cling.

Odo Cling was upright as a nail. He strained back on the leash, keeping the blood-red eager Cat in check. It writhed along the Lizard Path, sinuous as a lizard. It raised its head and gave its unearthly scream.

'It has your scent,' Brand cried. 'Quickly, Breeze. Get her on the path. I will take the rear.'

'No yer won't,' Jimmy Jaspers said. 'I got me axe. No pussy's scarin' me. I'm gunner have a whack at Odo Cling.'

'No,' Brand cried, 'you're crazy. The Cat is like nothing you have ever seen. It will have you torn in half before you can blink.'

'Yer reckon? I got a trick or two.'

But he hefted his pack and started after the others. Brand brought up the rear. They ran desperately, Breeze leading, then Susan and Nick. The path was only a foot-pace wide. Wildwood yawned at their feet. A wrong step would send them spinning down.

'Too slow,' Brand yelled. 'Throw away your packs.'

'Me meat,' Jimmy Jaspers said.

'And my brush that Brightfeather gave me,' Susan cried.

'Throw them. The Bloodcat will be on us.'

There was no space on the path to put them down. They dropped them over the edge, and they fell, turning lazily, down, down, towards the distant treetops.

'Move!' Brand yelled.

They ran on. Jimmy had his axe, and Susan her feather, and the goat-leather belt with the Half inside. That was all that was left of Morninghall. She could not believe the nightmare had started again. That chase up the path to the Living Hill – now this. It was as if nothing had happened between, that safe time with the Birdfolk only a dream. The Bloodcat was screaming continuously. She felt as if she wanted to leap off the path and fall for ever down to the safety of Wildwood.

'How close are they?'

'About five minutes back. Maybe ten.'

'Nick, we're going to get caught.'

'We'll have to fight.' But he knew it would be impossible. How could they fight on a path as narrow as this? One wrong step and you'd need a parachute. The Halfmen would get them one by one – Brand and Jimmy first. That axe would be no good, there was no room to swing it. Then him. Then Breeze. He saw them falling, with their arms outspread. He seemed to hear a wailing scream, fading away to nothing. What would it be like to be dead? And Susan would be left – alone with Odo Cling and his Halfmen; and the Cat.

'Keep moving. We'll get away.'

They came round a bulge in the cliff. It was like running in space. Two folds back the Halfmen slid from view. The Bloodcat's screaming thinned and died. A steady dull thunder filled the air. It was the noise of a waterfall; it was the Mountain's Grief. It came down from the cliff-top, hundreds of metres above, dropping straight in a groove cut in the cliff, and fell away, broken and foaming, into Wildwood. A wooden foot-bridge ran across it, half a dozen metres out from the water.

They ran through misty spray, ran on the slippery planks. Nick looked down. The moving water drew him into the forest. It seemed miles below. He felt his stomach falling. Brand gripped his arm and shoved him on.

'Jimmy!' Brand cried. It was no more than a thin bird-cry in the thundering water. Nick looked back. Jimmy had stopped on the far side of the bridge. He had taken a grip on his axe.

'Jimmy,' Nick screamed, 'you can't fight them.'

But Jimmy grinned. He gave his shoulders a flex. He yelled something that was torn away by the water.

'Stop him, Brand.' Susan and Breeze had come back. The four stood helplessly on the narrow path.

'We'll have to leave him.'

'No.'

Then Nick laughed. 'He's not going to fight. He's going to chop the bridge down.'

Jimmy swung his axe. With a couple of blows he loosened the first two planks of the deck and sent them spinning away. They had been fixed with spikes to two slender beams, the trunks of trees, that ran the full length of the bridge. Jimmy jumped on to one of the trunks and set his feet apart. He was agile as a monkey. The water roared at his back, Wildwood lay hundreds of metres below. He took no notice. He swung his axe and brought it down between his feet. It bit deeply into the log. He loosed it, swung again.

'The underhand chop,' Nick yelled. 'He told me he could do it.'

'He'll get marooned over there.'

'No he won't. He'll get back.'

Chips the size of dinner plates sprang in the air. Jimmy hopped neatly, turning about. He faced the waterfall and chopped into the other side of the log. But he did not cut right through. He left a centimetre of wood holding the beam. He stepped across and started on the other.

'Hurry, Jimmy,' Nick screamed. The Halfmen and the Bloodcat had come round the cliff, only one fold away. They would be here in a moment. Brand loosened his knife in its sheath. But Jimmy chopped precisely, without hurry. He jumped about, and swung his axe again. Chips of wood jumped out and fell away. Again he left the beam secured by a centimetre of wood. He ran along the bridge.

'Gimme some room.'

'Jimmy, you're marvellous.'

'Told yer I knowed a trick or two. Get back or yer'll 'ave no 'ead.' He smashed the planks, stepped on to the log. This time he chopped right through. The bridge made a shrieking sound and sagged a little on its outer side. 'One more,' Jimmy yelled. He stepped on to the last log. The wood was yellow as cheese and seemed to cut as easily. Half a dozen blows:

a deep V appeared in one side. Jimmy hopped. He swung again, just as Odo Cling and the Cat appeared round the bulge in the cliff.

'Jimmy, hurry, hurry.'

Jimmy chopped. One, two, three, four blows. He left a centimetre of wood again, and the bridge stayed, groaning, in its place. He jumped back on to the path. 'There. One more whack an' she's down.'

'Jimmy, do it, do it.'

Jimmy grinned. He leaned on his axe. He was sweating. 'I reckon I broke me record. Wish they coulda seen me at Fells Bush.'

'Jimmy!' Cling was a dozen steps away. The Bloodcat was straining on its leash.

'I will,' Jimmy said. 'When that Cling gets on.' He lifted his axe and faced the bridge, grinning. 'Gidday, Cling,' he yelled. 'Reckon yer caught us this time.'

But Cling stopped. His red eyes glared at the bridge, then at Jimmy. The Bloodcat leaned forward on its leash. Cling struck it on its snout with his whip, and it sank dog-like at his feet, but kept its glowing eyes fixed on Susan.

Then Cling beckoned behind him, where his dozen Half-men stood in file. The path was wider at both ends of the bridge. A Halfman slipped by him. Cling pointed and the man raised his knife, gave a soundless yell, and jumped the gap on to the planks. The beams held. He came across the slippery bridge, quick as an eel in water. Jimmy met him easily. He stood on the path and swung his axe in a way that seemed almost careless, and sent the man spinning away into space with a single blow. He seemed to float down slowly to the forest, his knife point still winking in the sun.

'Come on, Cling,' Jimmy yelled, 'it's you I want, not yer office boys.'

Cling shook his whip in the air. He raised his foot and seemed as if he would jump on to the bridge. But again he stopped. He snarled back at his men and pulled the Bloodcat aside. They ran by him, their red eyes shining with hatred, and jumped one by one on to the bridge, and poured across.

'Jimmy,' Susan screamed.

'Yeah, OK,' Jimmy said, ''ere we go.'

The first man was only a pace from him when the axe came down. It sliced clean as a knife through the centimetre of timber, and from the other side of the bridge came a sound like the crack of a stock-whip. The beams broke, the bridge fell.

It went nose first, and seemed to ride down the smoking water like a raft. The Halfmen turned about it like a cluster of black flies. Down, down they went, falling into Wildwood, disappearing into the mist of water over the treetops.

Jimmy and Odo Cling faced each other across the Mountain's Grief. Jimmy laughed. 'I reckon that's one up ter me, Cling. Now why don't yer come across? Don't yer know how ter fly?'

Cling crouched. His iron and leather glittered in the sun. For a moment it seemed he would jump. Hatred radiated from him. It made Susan shrink back against Breeze. Then Cling reached down to the Bloodcat and snapped the leash from its collar. The Cat came to its feet and stood there, trembling. It leaned out over the gap.

'Kill!' Cling shrieked. 'Kill!' The sound came sharp as knives through the roaring water.

'Run,' Brand cried, 'He has released the Cat.'

'It can't jump over that,' Nick said. The gap was fifteen metres at least.

'A Cat can jump anything. Run. Take Susan. Run.'

The Cat turned. It raced back along the path. It glowed like lava pouring from a mountain. Then it spun about, striking sparks with its claws on the stone. It started to run, it came up to the gap with the speed and beautiful ease of a charging tiger. Its eyes blinded them. It was like looking into a furnace On all that run, they never shifted from Susan, cowering against Breeze, a dozen steps behind Brand and Jimmy Jaspers.

Jimmy gave a yell. He sent Brand staggering back with a shove. 'Gimme some room.' He raised his axe above his head.

The Cat reached Odo Cling. It came to the gap. It launched itself on a gigantic leap and came like fire through the smoking air. Its mouth was stretched back in a snarl and its claws curved out like knives.

The length of that leap took Jimmy by surprise. The Cat went over him, a metre above his head, coming down in an arc that would end at Susan's throat. Even so, Jimmy had time to move. He stepped one pace back and swung his axe in a fierce upward cut. He had meant to take the Cat on its neck but the blow came down behind its shoulders. It was enough. The axe sank deeply in between the ribs. Then it was ripped away from Jimmy's hands. It clanged on the cliff and leaped out over the forest. And the Bloodcat? Jimmy had not struck it a mortal blow, but the force of it pushed the animal off course – pushed it out over empty air.

Susan felt blood spatter her face. She saw the snarling mask of the Cat flash by her eyes, saw the fire-red body twist, and a hind paw lash at her, and felt the point of a claw nick her on the throat. Then the Cat was gone. It vanished over the edge of the path and out of their sight as if it had become invisible. All that was left was a wailing cry, fading like a siren.

No one moved. Then Jimmy Jaspers pushed himself away from the cliff-face where he had tumbled. He went to the edge of the fall and faced Odo Cling. He took his clasp knife from his pocket and opened the blade.

'I still got me knife, Cling. Come on over. I'll even tie one 'and behind me back.'

9

Throat of the Underworld

They came down from the Lizard Path late in the afternoon. Instead of keeping south to the Sink Holes, Brand led them into Wildwood. At dusk they came to a Woodland village. It was hidden in a valley shaded by giant trees. The Woodlanders welcomed them. Breeze dressed the cut on Susan's throat. Then they sat about the fire, talking quietly of their flight from the Halfmen. Jimmy Jaspers was morose. He complained about his lost meat, and seemed to be mourning his axe.

'Jimmy, you were great,' Nick said. 'I've never seen anything so brave.'

'It was Cling I wanted, an' 'e got away.'

'Where will he go?' Susan asked Brand.

'He has men at Sheercliff. He will go there.'

'I reckon I could catch 'im if I started now. I'd make 'im squeal.'

'No,' Brand said, 'Wildwood is too big. You would never find him. Jimmy, do not sulk. We will make songs about your fight. No one has ever slain a Bloodcat before.'

'Lost me axe,' Jimmy said. 'Best axe I ever 'ad.'

The Woodlanders brought them food. They slept warm in leafy beds. Next morning they rested, and set out for the Sink Holes in the early afternoon.

'There's no hurry,' Brand said. 'The Stonefolk will not come out in the sunlight.'

They walked through open forest for several hours and came to a place of tangled underbrush and weathered boulders. 'Now we are heading into limestone country,' Brand said. 'The streams run underground. Do not stray from my path, there are sink holes everywhere.'

They saw the holes plunging into the earth, moss-grown, with cobwebs at their mouths. They came on them suddenly, and Brand slowed his pace, leading them carefully by the gaping pits. Here and there were ponds surrounded with reeds. Weed grew smoothly over them, making them look like putting greens on golf courses. They looked solid enough to picnic on.

'Do not go close. Hungry things live there.'

The land began to slope down. 'Now we are coming to it,' Brand said. 'The mighty Hole. Some call it Stonegut Deep. But Woodlanders call it the Throat of the Underworld. Freeman Wells came here and summoned the Stonefolk.'

'What do they look like?' Nick asked.

'I do not know. No Woodlander has ever seen them. No one has seen them.'

'Except Freeman Wells,' Nick said.

'Even he did not see.'

They followed a dry creek bed and came to a place where fallen boulders choked it. Beyond was a basin of cliffs, smooth as glass. Nick could not see any way to go forward. Brand stopped.

'We will wait here till dark.'

'What's over those boulders?' Nick asked.

'The Throat of the Underworld.'

'I'm going to see.'

'Be careful. The sight alone could make you fall.'

Nick scrambled up the boulders. He stood on top and looked across at the encircling cliffs. They went down, but he could not see how far. He took another few steps, vaulted easily to a lower boulder – and the hole opened up. He almost fell to his knees in fright. Its mouth was wide as the crater at Morninghall. Battleships could have been dropped in it. It was like the hungry gulping throat of the world. He felt it sucking him in, he was being sucked down into darkness, and he swayed and lurched a step towards the hole.

Brand jumped down beside him. He gripped his arm. 'Easy, Nick.'

'It's – it's impossible.'

'It is the Throat. As natural as a mountain or a river.'

'But it just – it just goes *down*.'

'Yes.'

'How far? I'm going to throw a stone in.'

'No. The Stonefolk would be angry.'

'How deep is it?'

'Freeman Wells said if you fell your heart would beat a hundred times before you struck the bottom.'

'Does Susan have to go down there?'

'Yes, Nick.'

'She can't. It's impossible.'

'The Stonefolk will guide her.'

Nick heard a noise and looked round. Susan was standing a little above him. She stared white-faced into the hole.

'I can't see any path,' she whispered.

'There is no path. The walls are smooth.'

'Then how do they take me down?'

'I don't know. But they guided Freeman Wells. The dark is coming, Susan. Let us see if we can speak with them. Stand at my side.'

She came down and took her place, leaning slightly against him. Brand put his arm around her. 'Don't be afraid. We have a saying: "Stoneman is the stone." They never fall. They will look after you.' He took her a step closer to the hole. He did not raise his voice but deepened it. 'Hail, Stonefolk of the Underworld. I am Brand of Wildwood. I break the ancient silence in the cause of Freeman Wells. I have a child with me. Her name is Susan Ferris. She wears the Mark of Freeman Wells, and she would have the Half left in your care.' His voice bounced off the cliffs and made a hollow rattle as it echoed in the Throat. Then there was silence. It went on and on.

'Maybe they're not at home,' Nick said.

Brand smiled. 'They heard. Quiet now, their answer comes.'

From deep down a gentle breathing sounded. It grew and grew, amplifying to the noise of a wind. Yet the air was still. No movement showed in the leaves of small trees growing here and there from cracks in the stone. Then in that gale of sound they heard a single drawn-out word take shape. It breathed its message, faded, and was gone. 'Stay-ay-ay.' After that dark sound the silence seemed to glitter.

'Is that all?' Nick said softly.

'Yes. They know we're here. Now we must wait. They will not come till dark, and even then not till the moon is down. Light of any kind gives them pain.' He turned Susan round. 'Let us go back to Breeze. She will have food for us.'

They climbed back over the boulders. Jimmy had lit a fire in the creek-bed and Breeze had a meal cooking. They ate in the gathering darkness. Susan sat close to the fire. She imagined a dreadful cold coming from the hole. Yet she knew she would go down. She had the strength of the Birdfolk. She had the feather, hanging now on Woodlander thread from her throat. And in her belt she had the good Half. It was nothing without the bad. She must have that too.

'Moonset in three hours,' Breeze said. 'Sleep a while, Susan. We will wake you.'

'Yes. All right.' She wrapped herself in her blanket and lay down with her back to the fire. She felt the Throat of the Underworld drawing her. She understood her fear, but could not understand her strange eagerness. The fire died down. She dozed a while, dreaming of sunlight and waterfalls, and woke with Breeze's hand on her shoulder.

'The moon is down, Susan. We must go.'

She unwrapped herself from her blanket but remained warm in her Woodlander cloak. Nick was sleeping. She did not wake him. Jimmy Jaspers looked up grumpily from the embers. 'See if yer can bring me somethin' ter eat.'

'Goodbye, Jimmy.'

She climbed the boulders between Brand and Breeze.

'Won't there be too much starlight?'

'Yes. They won't like it. But they'll come.'

'There are clouds coming,' Breeze said. 'It will be stone-black soon.'

They waited above the Throat, standing close together. Clouds came up and moved across the sky. The stars went out one by one. The only sound they heard was their own breathing. Then, at last, the Throat began to breathe. It was soft, an exhalation almost unheard, like the breathing of a sleeping child.

'Someone comes,' Breeze whispered.

The sound grew louder, moving about them like a shifting of air. With it came the faintest sound of stickiness; a gripping and release.

'They climb the walls.'

Susan shivered as the sounds came closer. Then she sensed something in front of her and strained her eyes to see. Nothing showed in the blackness. A wet touch came on her wrist. She almost screamed. But she held her arm still, and a second touch came on her and traced the outline of her birthmark.

'Yes,' breathed a voice at her side. It snuffled a moment in a staid excitement. 'Yes, it is the Mark. We must take you to the one who guards the Half.'

'Who,' Susan whispered, 'who are you?'

'I am Seeker,' the voice said wetly.

'And I,' snuffled another, 'I am Finder. We will take you down the Throat.'

'How?'

'You will not fall.'

'We have brought you wraps made of stone-worm silk. These were worn by Freeman Wells. None has worn them since.'

Something soft was pushed into her hands.

Breeze said, 'Marna told me of stone-worms. Their silk is spun from stone and seeks the stone.' She felt the silky things in Susan's hands. 'They are gloves and stockings. Pull them on your hands and feet.' She helped Susan separate the wraps. There were four, shaped like tubes and light as cheesecloth. Susan slipped her hand in one as far as her elbow. It was loose at first, but slowly it closed on her as if it were alive, and squeezed like rubber round her fingers and arm.

'It will not come off,' snuffled Seeker or Finder. 'Not till you command it.'

She put on the other wrap.

'Now your feet. Take your shoes off,' Breeze said.

She sat down and slipped her sneakers and socks off. Breeze gave her the wraps and she drew them on. They were exactly like stockings. They came over her knees. Slowly they tightened and held her firm. She stood up. 'Breeze, I can't move my feet.'

'That is why you will not fall,' Brand said. 'Touch the boulder with your hands.'

She did, and was locked there, like a fly on fly-paper.

'Stone-silk calls to stone, and stone calls silk,' said Seeker Finder.

'But how will I move?'

'Command the silk. Tell it to let go.'

'Let go,' Susan cried.

'Think it, child. In your mind,' Breeze said.

'And only one wrap at a time, not all four,' Brand said. 'Otherwise you will fall.'

'She will not fall,' the Stonemen said, 'not with Stonefolk guarding her.'

'Tell it to let go, Susan.'

So she thought of her right hand, and whispered in her mind: *Let go*, and her hand came free. *Let go*, she told her left.

'This is easy.' She walked about the boulder, commanding

her feet. She laughed. 'This is easy.' But then one of the Stonemen said, 'You are at the edge. Now we will go,' and she felt herself begin to shake and she cried out, 'No, not yet. Breeze, I don't want to go.'

'You will not fall. They will watch,' Breeze said.

'Stoneman is the stone,' Brand said softly.

'Stoneman is the stone,' said Seeker/Finder. 'Come, we must be gone.'

She felt their damp hands settle on her skin. But one at least had a friendly touch. 'We will not let you fall.' They made her kneel and push her feet out over the Throat. Her hands were locked on the stone, but slowly, as the Stonemen held her, she inched them back until they were on the edge. Her body was in space, supported by Finder and Seeker. Then her feet found stone and locked in place. She was on the wall of the Throat. She felt as if she were floating there, in a well full to its brim with thick black water. Somewhere just above her Brand and Breeze moved about – on horizontal rock, in another dimension.

'Brand, Breeze.'

'Yes, Susan. Goodbye. You will come back soon.'

'Wait here. Please.'

'No,' one of the Stonemen said. 'We will not bring her up the wall. Wait at the place where the River Stoneblood leaves the stone.'

Then they started down. They moved Susan between them like a sack of old clothes. Their hands and feet made faint plopping sounds. She felt them scuttling about her as briskly as mice on a floor. The likeness brought her comfort. It even made her smile, and soon she said, 'I think I can do it now,' and she began to fix and shift her hands of her own accord. The attraction between stone-silk and stone was so strong that her palms darted the last few inches and smacked on the wall of the Throat, locking her in place from fingertips to elbow. Her legs were the same. She found it easier to point her toes and let her instep, shins and knees fasten on the stone. So they travelled down. Only now and then the knowledge of where she was made her gasp with a sudden terror and try to curl her fingers into the rock. Then the Stonemen held her and they waited still as lizards on the face until she was ready to go on.

What had Brand said? The Throat was a hundred heartbeats deep? She heard her own heart beating. It seemed they had spent hours on the wall. Now and then one of the Stonemen breathed a word, telling her of some lump or hollow in the rock. One of them made a soft asthmatic whistle as he spoke. Although she was only guessing, she called him Seeker. He became her favourite. Finder was more bossy. Once when she released a hand too soon he dug her sharply in the ribs. She gave a little scream, but it was mostly from fright. The sound bounced like a ball round the Throat, and fell away, booming faintly. She felt almost sick with discouragement. There was still a long way to go.

But it was done at last. In that woolly blackness – and the air was warmer than outside the Throat – she heard a flattening of sound. It took a wooden quality, as though it had no depth.

'Are we near the bottom?'

'Almost there,' Seeker breathed.

She stumbled as she came off the wall. She had grown so used to making certain movements that walking normally was something she could not manage.

'You come from a clumsy race,' Finder said sourly.

'I can't see.'

'Follow us.'

'How do your eyes work in the dark?'

'We have no eyes. We have no need of them.'

'There are other ways of seeing,' Seeker said.

For the first time since starting she looked up. Perhaps the clouds had moved. Perhaps she would see the stars. That would make her feel better. But there was nothing.

'Come,' Seeker wheezed. 'I will lead. Finder will follow. Do not try to see. Close your eyes and walk. We will tell you when to stop.'

'Shall I take these gloves and things off?'

'No. There is climbing to do.'

They started off. Seeker kept up a faint humming noise, guiding her. It was hard walking in the stone-silk stockings, they fixed her to the floor and would not let her go until she signalled them. And when her hands brushed against the walls she found herself stuck there. Several times she was jerked off balance. She folded her arms tightly on her chest and kept them there. But soon she found why the gloves and shoes were necessary. Finder pushed her up against a wall and told her to climb. She went up and along, and for a few moments, unbelievably, out. She felt herself hanging from a ceiling and heard water rushing beneath her. Then she had to turn her body slowly round and come down feet first on the other side of what she supposed had been an underground river.

They walked again. Seeker wheezed and snuffled like a hedgehog. Finder dug her in the ribs with his horny finger. Many times she heard water. It dripped and roared and hissed. She heard it making a throaty boom deep in a gorge, and felt its spray on her face from a waterfall. The feet of her guides made sticky rubber sounds. She wished she could see them, and imagined them pink and hairless, naked as new-born possums, or like kewpie dolls, with heads like balloons.

'Where are we?'

'In Stoneworld. Under the place you call Wildwood.'

'Is it morning yet?'

'There is no morning in Stoneworld.'

They went on. The passages seemed to grow narrower. Her head grazed a ceiling and she gave a cry. She could not tell whether the moisture in her hair was water or blood.

'Stupid human,' Finder said.

But Seeker made a noise of sympathy. 'I am sorry child. You are taller than us. We should have thought.'

'Is it far?'

'Watcher's cell is under the River Stoneblood.'

'I'm hungry.'

'Our food would poison you. Freeman Wells tried it and was ill.'

'When will we come out?'

'In the time you call afternoon.'

'Watcher waits,' Finder said. 'Let us talk less and travel more.'

They padded on again. There was more climbing, more booming of water, and an echoing cavern that sounded, Susan thought, a mile across. Now and then other Stonefolk passed her. She felt their damp fingers on her skin. Then came the gentle sound of water moving without hurry. There was a lapping, and soft slapping, and sounds of Stonefolk laughing.

'The River Stoneblood,' Seeker said. 'The children play.'

Susan felt small bodies moving about her knees. She smiled. She had not thought of the Stonefolk as having children.

They followed the River Stoneblood for a long while. It flowed along silkily, lapping idly – strange for a river with such a fierce name. Along its side was a road thronged with Stonefolk. Susan guessed they had come in from their passages and halls to see her pass – if see was the word. She felt like a queen on a royal tour. But after a while the river began to flow more swiftly, she could tell from its hissing sound, and the Stonefolk were left behind. She and Finder and Seeker kept on through lonely caverns.

At last Seeker said, 'Climb.' She felt her way up a sloping wall, slick with running water. 'Now down.' She went down another wall, dry this time. It plunged deep and seemed to turn under the river, into a honeycomb of passages. There were broken echoes and sudden reverberations. Seeker stopped. He put back his hand and held Susan still.

'Watcher. Old One. Your pain is done. Your task is over. We bring a human female, with the Mark of Freeman Wells burned on her skin.'

There was a shuffling in the dark – a slow sound, like the noise of a sick old animal turning in a bed of straw. Feet came tiredly towards them.

'A human female,' said a voice, dusty as old books. 'She is a child. Are you sure? Let me see the Mark.'

Susan put out her arm. She began to roll the stone-silk glove down her forearm, but Seeker said, 'No. He can see through that.' She felt Watcher's touch. It was light and prickly as a crawling insect yet had the dampness of worms. She tried not to shiver.

'Yes, yes,' quavered the voice, 'it is the Mark. The true Mark. I had thought you would never come.' His hands wandered over her face. 'And you have the good Half already. I can feel it in you. May Stonegod grant you have strength for the bad.'

'I have strength,' Susan said, in a trembling voice.

'Ah child, you release me. I have watched the Half while time grew old. Well, so it seems to me. I know that I am ancient, and ready to die now my task is done. You bring me a gift greater than you know. Give me your hand now. Take the glove off. I will place your fingers on the Half.'

She peeled off the glove. Someone took it from her – Seeker, she guessed. Watcher took her hand. But she said, 'Wait.' She took the other glove off and fumbled the good Half from her pouch. She held it tightly in her hand. 'Now.'

'Ah yes, the good Half. That is wise. It will give you strength.'

And she felt strength flowing through her. It travelled rich and warm through her body, along her limbs. It throbbed behind her eyes, in the blackness of her head.

Watcher took her hand again. He guided her through the

dark. She felt as if she were drowning in black oil, but she kept on.

'Here, child.' He pushed her hand gently, firmly, down. She felt the Half with her fingertips. It lay waist high, on a flat stone table. She traced its outline – that curved teardrop now so familiar to her. Watcher's hand withdrew. She picked up the Half.

At once she felt that tearing apart of herself, that breaking up she had felt in the cave on Mount Morningstar. But this was worse. She felt herself spinning as if in that whirlpool between the worlds, and parts of her, brain, tongue, heart, bowels, went whirling away, each crying on its own in a dreadful agony. She felt Watcher holding her, and Seeker holding her. It was no help. She heard herself scream. She heard *herself*. And that was the good Half's doing. The good Half was holding her together, the good Half was showing her herself. She screamed again. She screamed as a message to Susan Ferris. Watcher's chamber echoed with her screams. And slowly, slowly, with infinite pain, she came back together, all her whirling parts swam into place and fitted in, and she was whole. She sank sobbing down upon the floor.

Watcher's old voice whispered sadly about her. 'That was great pain you endured. You are brave. Freeman Wells chose wisely. It is done now. Put the Half away. The evil in it sprang to life and tried to destroy you, as it has tried to destroy me. But it can do no harm now. You have drawn it into balance.'

'I felt – I felt –' Susan sobbed.

'I know what you felt. Put it away.' His damp old hands patted her soothingly. She slipped the Halves into her belt and buckled the pouches. Seeker helped her to her feet.

'We must go now. We must get you back to food and light.' The word made him tremble. 'Watcher, Old One, rest. Finder and I will return and take you to the deepest dark of all. Stone must thank you for your agony.'

The old Stoneman made a strange sound – perhaps a laugh.

'Ah, ah, speeches. Ceremonies. No thank you, young Stoneman. Not for me. I require no thanks. I will wait here for the final news. This child still has her task before her. We will not celebrate till that is done. It would not be seemly.'

'Thank you,' Susan said. 'Thank you for guarding the Half.'

'Mine was the easy part.'

Seeker took her hand and slipped the stone-gloves on her. He turned her about. She moved like a zombie and could not tell in which direction Watcher stood.

'Goodbye,' she said.

'Goodbye, human child. Carry all the strength of Stone with you.' She heard again a tired dusty turning as he sank upon the floor. 'I will sleep, though it is a selfish thing to do.'

Seeker led her out of the chamber, setting up his soft humming again. Finder prodded her up the wall. They came down to the river. Susan heard it slithering like a snake. She felt the Halves in her belt, dragging her down. She felt as if she were stumbling under huge weights.

'Wake up,' Finder said bad-temperedly.

'I can't go any faster.'

'Do not bully her,' Seeker said, 'or by Great Stone I'll stamp upon your toes. Come Susan, we must keep moving. Your friends are waiting in the light. It is not far.'

They hurried on beside the river. Hours seemed to pass. Susan kept her eyes tightly closed. Her head was filled with sparkling stars and thoughts of food and drink. The echoes from the walls smacked like hands. They crossed the river several times. Once they climbed high along a wall that seemed to overhang it, and then went through narrow clefts with water rumbling far below. Stone kept snatching at her arms. When they came down she was so tired Seeker let her rest a while. But the way was easier after that. It followed the river. Images kept turning through her head, feathers, water sparkling in glass jugs, human faces. They floated sideways, upside down. She wondered if she were sleeping as she walked.

At last Seeker said, 'We are nearly there.'

Finder stopped. 'I can go no further. This filthy light is stuck all over me.'

'Light?' Susan said stupidly. She turned her eyes all round. The dark was as thick as ever.

'We have come far enough,' Finder said.

'Go back,' Seeker said. 'I shall take her to the entrance.'

'You will stink of it when you come back.'

'Then I shall stink. Go. Leave us alone.'

Susan heard Finder padding away.

'Do not blame him,' Seeker said. 'We fear the light above all other things.'

'I can't see any light.'

'It is here. I can take you only a little way. Then I must go back too.'

She heard him set off. There seemed to be a desperation in his humming now. In a moment she heard him give a grunt of pain.

'Is it hurting you?'

'Yes. Yes. It hurts. I must stop soon.' He kept on a little way. And she began to feel a lessening of the darkness. The faintest tinge of grey came into it. Seeker gave a wheezy cry. 'I can go no further. It burns me to the marrow of my bones.'

'I think I can see it now.'

'Yes. It is your afternoon out there. Susan, I must turn back or die. Follow the light. You will come out soon.'

'I – I think I can see you.' But it was only a shapeless stain on the grey. She could make out no features.

'I am nothing to see. You would find me ugly. Goodbye, Susan.' The patch of darkness started to move away.

'Wait. The gloves. The stone-silk.'

'They are yours. Our gift. You may find use for them. Goodbye.' His voice breathed damply in the cavern and

137

shrank away to whispers. Then there was nothing but the soft rush of the river.

'Goodbye,' Susan said. She sank on her knees and rested a while. Then she began to move towards the light. It swelled and burned her eyes. She narrowed them and hurried on. The grey river ran at her side. A light painful as acid sprayed from its surface. She turned her head away, and felt her way forward along the walls. But soon even stone hurt her to look at. She had to close her eyes. She wondered if she would ever be able to bear the light again.

Slowly she went towards the afternoon. Light glared redly through her closed eyelids. She took her hands off the walls and covered her face and stumbled on. She did not know if she was walking towards the outside world or the river.

'Nick!' she began to cry. 'Brand! Breeze!'

Soon she heard them calling, and heard their feet running on the stone.

10

Wings

Nick and Susan sat on a grassy hillside above the Woodland village called Shady Home. It was Brand's and Breeze's village. Dale and Verna lived there too. Susan had travelled in a dream through Wildwood, two days from the portals of the River Stoneblood to Shady Home. On the first day Breeze kept bandages on her eyes. To make better speed Brand and Jimmy Jaspers carried her on a rough stretcher. She was able to see better the second day. She insisted on walking, but it was not till evening that she began to come properly into the world of light. It was Verna hugging her, and Woodland children playing in the trees, and the smoke of cooking fires, and the sight of coloured clothing hung out to dry, fluttering like flags in the trees, that made her understand at last that she was back in a world where things were normal and light and colour were good.

She slept that night in Breeze's house, high in the branches of a giant tree. The wind rocked her to sleep. In the morning she woke and saw the sun, and sighed, and slept again.

'It was a sickness I do not understand,' Breeze said to Nick. 'But she is better now.'

Nick rested on the grass. He was not sure. Her cheeks were pale and her eyes burned brightly. He was sure her arms and legs had not been so thin. And she handled the two Halves obsessively, but locked them in her fists when he asked to see. He had only glimpsed the bad Half – deep red, almost black, with a spot of golden-white submerged in it. It had made him shiver unaccountably.

The morning sun burned down on their heads. At the foot

of the hill Woodland children splashed in the glass–clear water of the stream.

'Come and have a swim,' Nick said.

'No.' She clicked the Halves in her hands like beads. 'Nick, I've got to go soon. I can't wait here.'

'I know.'

'The Halves were sleeping. When they woke they woke something up in me. I've got to go to the Motherstone. It's calling me.'

'We'll go. Brand has got his scouts out. They'll find a way.'

'I can't wait long.'

Brand and Jimmy crossed the stream and walked up the hill to them. They sat down on the grass.

'The scouts are back,' Brand said. 'The news is bad. Cling and his men are patrolling the top of Sheercliff. He has guards blocking all the pathways down. We cannot go that way.'

Susan had put the Halves in their pouches. She had taken the Birdfolk feather from her throat and was turning it in her fingers. 'Can't we slip by them?'

'I could grab that Cling and chuck 'im orf the cliff,' Jimmy said. 'They wouldn' 'ave no leader then.'

'No, there are too many. And we can't slip by. The paths are narrow. We have to find another way.'

'I can go by myself,' Susan said.

'No.'

'I can,' she said. 'I can climb. I've got the stone-silk gloves.'

'They'd swat yer like a fly,' Jimmy said.

'They watch every place,' Brand said. 'Woodlanders used to climb Sheercliff for sport, and Cling knows that. He has men at every place you could go.'

'And you can't go alone,' Nick said. 'That's that. So think of something else.'

'Like parachutes,' Jimmy said.

'Ha,' Nick laughed. Then he stopped. He looked at the feather in Susan's hands. 'I've got it,' he said. 'We can fly.'

'The sun's gorn to 'is 'ead,' Jimmy said.

'No, wait a minute. We can make hang-gliders. I was thinking about it at Morninghall. I know all about hang-gliders. I've got a book at home. Dad said I could build one when I was older.'

'What are hang-gliders?' Brand asked.

'Like – like wings. They catch the air. You glide like a bird. They're fixed on frames. You don't have to flap.'

'Like a giant kite?' Brand said. 'There is a tale one of our ancestors, Deven was his name, launched himself from Sheercliff on a kite. He was never seen again.'

'No bloddy wonder,' Jimmy said.

'It'll work, Jimmy. Come on, Brand. Let's go down. I'll need the lightest wood you've got. And strong. And a lot of that cloth you weave. Come on, Susan. You too, Jimmy. You can help.'

It took Nick two days to build his prototype. Brand went into the forest and came back with a dozen rods of bamboo-like wood, light and tough as aluminium. Breeze and Verna gave lengths of pale blue cloth that Nick declared was better than dacron. Jimmy whittled with his knife and grumbled away. He bound the joints in the rods with cord. They were strong as welding. Late in the afternoon Nick stood on the hillside over the stream, with his wings spread like a butterfly. Susan had painted yellow suns on them. The whole population of the village had gathered to watch. Nick chose the place where the hill was steepest. He grinned at Susan confidently, but she noticed his hands trembled on the control bar.

'Wish me luck.' He ran down the slope and launched himself. And flew. Susan could hardly believe it. He flew down the hill and over the stream and circled in front of Shady Home, and landed neat as a seagull on the green. The Woodlanders clapped and cheered. Jimmy Jaspers gave a whoop.

Susan raced down the hill and hugged him. His face was red with excitement. But he said, 'Not good enough. That was just a glide. Now I've got to learn how to use the air currents and really fly.'

He practised until dusk. The blue glider vaulted over the stream. Once Nick flew down towards Sheercliff and Brand was worried Halfmen would see him. But he turned back. The breeze was lumpy over the forest. He barely had height to make it to Shady Home. One of his wings clipped a tree on the edge of the green and he spun crazily and landed in the stream. 'It'll be all right from Sheercliff. The wind will come up smooth over the smoke.'

Brand called the crafts-people of Shady Home to a meeting. 'We will work through the night. I will send out men to cut rods. Choose your strongest silk. By morning we will have gliders made for Susan and Breeze and me. And a large one for Jimmy Jaspers.'

''Old on,' Jimmy said. 'Yer didn' ask me. I'm not flyin' nowhere. I likes ter keep me feet on the ground.'

'Come on Jimmy, it's easy,' Nick said. 'You'll be good at it.'

'If I was meant ter fly I'd 'ave feathers like them Birdfolk. An' I'd probably lay eggs. No, yer can keep yer wings. An' I wish yer luck. Me, I'm goin' out after Odo Cling.'

'Jimmy, you can't.'

'You watch me.'

'He'll kill you.'

'Wrong, younker. I'll kill 'im. I got me knife. Brand says 'e's down at Sheercliff. So that's where I'm 'eadin'. Mebbe by the time yer gets there with yer fancy wings I'll 'ave 'im 'angin' in a tree fer dog tucker.'

Susan looked at his fierce old face, with its hanging lip and whiskery chin and bloodshot eyes. She reached out and took his hand. 'Jimmy, you killed the Bloodcat. You paid us back.'

'Yerss, reckon I did. I was a bloddy ratbag, girl. I been a ratbag all me life. But Cling made me worse. I got ter pay 'im out fer that. An' fer gettin' 'is boys ter pig-stick me. But I saved yer, so I don't owe yer nothin'. This is fer me. Reckon I won't be easy till I've settled with that joker.'

'Jimmy –'

'No use talkin' girl. I got me mind made up. Startin' in the mornin'. Now I'm gettin' some shut-eye. I gotter keep me strength up. All these veges I been eatin' has got me kinda weak in the knees. Next thing I'll be chewin' me cud like a bloddy cow.'

He got up and stumped off to his bed.

'Nick, Cling will kill him.'

'I don't know. Jimmy's pretty tough. He killed the Bloodcat.'

'That was luck. He will be no match for Cling,' Brand said gloomily. 'He does not understand evil. But we cannot stop him. So let us get the gliders made. I will take men out to cut the rods. Breeze and Verna, see about the cloth. And Susan, you had better get some sleep. You must learn to fly tomorrow.'

Jimmy set off early in the morning. Susan and Nick walked through Shady Home with him. He had a blanket rolled on his back and a bag of dried fern root in his hand. 'Don't tell Breeze,' he grinned, 'but I'm gunner chuck this away when I'm down the track. It don't agree with me.'

'What will you eat, Jimmy?'

The old man looked cunning. 'Yer can't tell me there ain't no deer in this bush. An' rabbits. I seen the signs. I reckon I can trap some. An' there's some juicy lookin' birds. An' eels in the creeks. An' trout. I'll live pretty good. Brand give me a firebox. I'll be scoffin' baked trout ternight. Then ole Cling better watch out. I'll twist 'is 'ead around so 'e'll be able ter watch the fleas crawlin' up 'is backside.'

'Be careful, Jimmy.'

143

'Don't yer worry about me. Watch out with them wings, yer hear?'

'We will.'

'See yer, then.' He set off down the track out of the village and disappeared in the trees. Nick and Susan walked back to the green where the Woodlanders were putting the final touches to the gliders. They felt vulnerable now that Jimmy was gone. Susan looked at her glider without confidence. 'I can't fly in that.'

'Sure you can,' Nick said, but looking at her he was anything but sure. She had grown so pale and thin.

The Woodlanders carried the gliders to the top of the hill. Susan's was made of green silk. Breeze had painted Shy flowers on it. Her own was pale gold and Brand's was brown. Nick explained the principles of hang-gliding to them. He had designed the slings for an upright position, not prone. The gliders were, he said, simple Rogallo types, with arrowhead, keel and cross-tube ... Susan stopped listening. They would work or they wouldn't. All she knew was that she must get down Sheercliff. If she could not fly she would have to climb. She felt the stone-silk gloves wrapped in a tiny bundle in her pocket. She did not believe Seeker had given them to her for nothing. He had foreseen a use for them.

'Now,' Nick said, 'I'll demonstrate. Then Brand and Breeze can follow me. Then Susan. Any questions?' There were none. He climbed into his harness and made a simple flight down to the green. 'Right,' he yelled, 'the wind's okay. Remember everything I said.'

Brand flew down, and Breeze. They did it perfectly. They were so light and quick, they were natural fliers. It was Susan's turn. She climbed into her harness and looked down the hill. Suddenly it was steep. Nick seemed tiny down there. She waved at him limply and gripped the bar. Then she started to run awkwardly, and was surprised at the weight above her and the way the wings buffeted and jerked. Then suddenly everything was smooth, she was lifted as though by a hand and was floating on air. The hillside fell away, the silver stream floated by, and the smooth grass of the green, with Nick and Brand and Breeze standing on it. Their gliders rested on the grass like giant butterflies sunning their wings. They waved their arms.

'Susan,' Nick yelled, 'pull your weight forward. You're going too far.'

But she went over them in a dream.

'Your weight. Shift your weight to one side.' She wondered why she should do that. It was lovely floating in the air. She felt she could fly right down to Darkland, down to the Mother-stone. Then she looked ahead and saw treetops rushing at her. They came with the speed of cars, and she screamed and flung her hands over her face. She felt a jolt that rattled her teeth. She heard the tearing of cloth and snapping of rods. She was tipped upside down, and she lay in the tree, cupped in the wings of her glider like a fish lying on a plate. She did not move. She felt even to speak might send her crashing down. Then she heard voices. Nick was calling from the ground. Brand and Dale and Verna were climbing up the tree. She heard them coming with the speed of squirrels. In a moment their faces popped up over the edge of the sail and goggled at her.

'Susan, are you all right?'

'Yes. Yes. Just get me out of here.'

They got her to the ground. Breeze examined her for cuts, but she was all right. Brand and Dale lowered the wrecked glider from the tree.

'Why didn't you shift your weight?' Nick raged. 'I explained it all. Forward and back when you want to go up and down. Sideways for turning.'

'I didn't listen.'

He could not believe it. He half turned away, with his hands on his hips. 'Well ... well ... of all the ...'

'You listen to me, Nick. I've got one thing on my mind. That's the Halves. And the Motherstone. I'm filled with that. There's no room for anything else. I can't listen. I can't concentrate.'

'You've got to –'

'No. I flew, didn't I? I got in that thing and flew. When I get to Sheercliff I'll do it again. And you can fly beside me and tell me how to turn and go up and down. That's all. I'm not going to practise any more.'

'Listen –'

'No.' She climbed to Breeze's house and lay down on her bed. She took the Halves from their pouches and held them on her chest. 'We'll get there.' She heard the sounds of the Woodlanders mending her glider. 'I'll fly if I have to. Or climb down holes. Or walk on water. We'll get to the Motherstone.' She slept.

The next morning they started out for Sheercliff. Susan was still in disgrace with Nick. He travelled with the Woodlanders bringing the gliders. That was not easy in the forest. They fell behind Susan and Brand and Breeze. Brand carried a pack holding four Halfman cloaks. Breeze had food in her pouch.

'But it won't last long. Once we get down there we'll have to move quickly. We will fly down to the coast and ask for help from the Seafolk. Perhaps they know a way into the city.'

'How will we breath?'

'I've sewn pads of Shy into the cloaks.'

'We have had spies in Darkland,' Brand said. 'Otis Claw holds a court each day. Halfmen bring their disputes to him and he judges them. It is his game. As likely as not he will order both parties slain or thrown to his dogs. Yet the Halfmen come. They come in great crowds, for sometimes when the whim takes him Claw gives great rewards. Or perhaps he will let one person slay his enemy on the spot. That amuses him too.'

'Odo Cling is a child beside him,' Breeze said, shivering.

'We will go to his court. We will slip in with the crowd. Then perhaps Susan will find a way to reach the Stone.'

Their day's march brought them close to Sheercliff. In the morning Brand sent out scouts. They came back with news that the way to the cliff was clear. Halfman squads were posted north and south, at the head of paths leading down to Darkland, but Cling had left the bluff called Deven's Leap unguarded. The cliff was undercut and could not be climbed.

They came to it in the afternoon. Deven's Leap was a huge stone forehead jutting over Darkland. Bush came half-way down it, like a fringe of hair. The brown smoke lay below, like greasy linoleum. It ran into the distance north and south, but opposite the Leap it narrowed like the waist of an hour-glass. Susan saw the blue shine of the sea.

'The smoke will not advance over the sea,' Brand said. 'Salt air destroys it. If we can reach the coast we will not need our Shy.'

Quietly the Woodlanders brought the gliders to the edge of the trees.

'Go now,' Brand said. 'We will fly at dusk. There will be a breeze from the sea. And moonlight for an hour. If we are lucky Odo Cling will not see us.'

Verna embraced Susan. The Woodlanders melted back into the forest. Nick crept along a narrow crack in Deven's Leap and chose a place for their take-off. When he came back he explained to Susan again about the mechanics of hang-gliding. She tried to listen. She was gloomy. It seemed to her this flight was reckless. Since she had had the Halves she had felt herself cut off from everyone. She took this as a sign that she must carry out her task alone. Nick and Brand and Breeze would hinder it. But there was no way she could get away from them. Brand brought out their Halfman cloaks. They were black as night. Susan trembled as she pulled hers over her head. She and Nick took off their sneakers. From now on they would have to travel barefooted. Breeze painted their faces and arms and legs with dye crushed from the bark of a tree.

'Now we look like Halfmen. When we are down there keep your hoods over your faces. Do not let the Halfmen see your eyes. There is no way I can colour those.'

The sun slipped fatly down to the fringe of the smoke. It turned a dusty red. Brand set out to scout along the cliff. 'When he comes back it will be time,' Breeze said. 'Eat something now. It may be long before we eat again.

But Susan was not hungry. She drank some water. Nick checked the gliders, going over every strut and joint. He was fussy as a clock-maker, but his eyes in his darkened face shone with excitement. She watched him like a stranger. For him this was just an adventure. She felt years older than him.

He came back and patted her. 'Remember Susan, it's all in the way you shift your weight. I'll fly beside you –'

'Quiet,' Breeze said.

'Don't move suddenly. Just a slight move is enough.'

'Quiet.' Her hand came over his mouth. 'That was Brand calling.'

They listened. Back in the forest came a ululating cry.

'The danger call,' Breeze said. 'Get the gliders out. Halfmen are coming.' She picked up Brand's and dragged it on to the Leap. Nick and Susan pulled out their own.

'Into them,' Breeze cried. 'Don't wait for me.' She ran back for her own glider. The cry came closer, urgent, desperate. Nick and Susan struggled with their harnesses. Susan could not manage hers. Nick ran to help her. Then Brand came tumbling from the bush. Deathguards were at his heels. Odo Cling's voice rang on the Leap.

'Do not kill them. I need them alive.'

The guards ran by them, cutting them off from the edge of the cliff. Nick and Susan, Brand and Breeze, were held as though in a noose. The Deathguards tightened in, jabbing with their knives.

'No,' Cling cried, 'obey me! Soon I will let you kill. I wish to talk with them first.' He strutted on to the Leap, flicking with his whip. 'So,' he said, 'it has been a long chase. But now your running stops. I have you, Mixies. And your pretty toys. Do they really fly? They will amuse Darksoul. But tell me where my friend Jimmy Jaspers is. He and I have a score to settle.'

'Stand back, Halfman,' Brand said. He had drawn his knife.

Cling laughed. 'You cannot fight us all. You vermin of the woods are quite amusing. Did you wish to fly? We shall let you fly in a moment or two. We shall smash your pretty wings first. Then we shall throw you off Sheercliff. You will get to Darkland after all, Woodlanders. And the Mixie boy will follow. But first, where is Jimmy Jaspers? I have promised myself great sport with him.'

'You'll never catch Jimmy.'

'We shall see. Take the Woodland hag and throw her off.'

Two Halfmen sprang at Breeze. But Susan jumped in front of her. She bared her arm. 'Get back or I'll burn you.' The Halfmen stopped. They crouched and thrust out their knives.

'You cannot fight us all,' Cling grinned. 'I have twenty men and you are four. But tell me, Susan Ferris, where are the Halves? You have them, that is plain. I see how they eat at you. Ah, Otis Claw will be pleased to have them back.'

'He'll never have the Halves,' Susan said. Her eyes darted about, over the panting faces of the Guards and Cling's red eyes, over the bush beyond. She smiled. She held up her arm, forcing every Halfman to look at it.

'See,' she said, 'see. The Halves have taught me many things.' She did not know what she was going to say next. It did not matter, as long as they kept on looking at her, as long as none of them shifted their eyes and saw Jimmy Jaspers coming fast and quiet, at a crouch, with his clasp knife in his hand, heading for Odo Cling. He came like a great shambling bear from the dark of the trees over the sunlit stone of Deven's Leap. His mouth was grinning wickedly. His eyes were set on Cling.

'Don't move,' Susan cried, 'or I'll lower my arm. The Halves will explode and kill us all.'

Cling laughed. The red of his eyes deepened with amusement. 'A clever tale, Mixie. Ah, you are clever. But I know about the Halves. I have studied them. They do not work in that way. They seek the Motherstone, that is all. But Darksoul will destroy them. And destroy you. Enough of your games now. Take her, bind her arms. Then we will see how well Woodlanders fly.'

One of the Halfmen sprang. She struck him with her arm and he exploded backwards. Before the others could move Jimmy Jaspers gave a roar. He was ten paces from Cling. He charged over the rock like a boar. He seized Cling in his arm and jerked him in the air. His knife came down and lay across Cling's throat. Nobody moved. Then Jimmy spoke.

'Tell yer zombies ter keep still Cling, or I'll gut yer like a chook.'

Cling was making choking noises. His arms and legs beat like paddles.

'Keep still, yer little bogger.' Jimmy's arm tightened on Cling's chest. He pressed his knife down half a centimetre. Grey blood trickled on Cling's throat. 'Tell 'em ter get back. An' tell 'em ter get away from me friends.'

'Back,' Cling croaked. 'Do as he says.'

His Deathguards had come at Jimmy in a pack. They bristled with knives, their grey teeth gleamed. They crouched and wove like boxers looking for an opening.

'Back. I'll slice 'is gizzard.'

And Cling, his eyes popping, cried again, 'Do as he says. He will kill me.' His throat worked against Jimmy's knife and blood ran thickly down. His arms and legs had stopped their beating and now worked slow and spiky. He was like an insect lying on its back.

'Get over ter the edge of the cliff,' Jimmy yelled. 'Go on, yer miserable sods, all of yer. Make one move at me friends an' yer boss is a goner. That's right, nice an' slow.'

The Halfmen backed away. They snarled like a pack of dogs. They worked their jaws. Jimmy began to follow them. He forced them back until they were at the edge of the Leap.

'I reckon they'd jump orf if yer gave the order, eh Cling? Go on, jump yer sods, the lot of yer.'

But the Halfmen snarled. They crouched ever lower, waiting for their chance.

'Be careful, Jimmy,' Susan whispered. But Jimmy was taking no chances. He kept back from the Guards. He hefted Cling higher and kept the knife firm against his throat. Cling's iron hat fell off. It clanged on the stone and bounced into space.

'That's where yer goin' Cling, if yer try any tricks. Now tell 'em ter chuck their knives orf. Go on, tell 'em.'

Cling croaked and wheezed. His grey bald scalp gleamed pathetically. 'Throw your knives. I order you. Throw them down.'

One by one the Halfmen obeyed. Their knives glittered as they fell towards the smoke. Jimmy laughed.

'If they lands on any of yer mates down there it's their bad luck. Now go on yer boggers, clear out. Get orf home an' I hope yer mothers spanks the lot of yer.'

The Halfmen milled about. Without their knives they seemed to have lost their will. They shambled in a pack well clear of Jimmy and made their way up to the edge of the bush.

Jimmy grinned at Nick and Susan. 'Now get in them hairy buzzers an' start flyin'.'

'Jimmy, you saved us,' Susan cried.

'Reckon I did, young Susie. I been trackin' Cling all day. Now I got 'im. You get goin', then I'll settle with 'im.'

'We can't leave you here, Jimmy.' She saw the Deathguards lurking in the trees like hungry wolves.

'Yes yer can. I got the drop on 'im. Reckon I might chuck 'im orf this cliff. 'E'll pass yer on the way down.'

'Jimmy –'

'Do as he says,' Brand said. 'He has given us our chance. Into your harness.'

Nick helped her. He positioned her at the edge of the Leap, then climbed into his own harness. The four stood poised at the drop like four great birds.

'Good luck,' Jimmy yelled. 'Don't go poopin' on anyone.'

'Be careful, Jimmy.'

'Yup,' Jimmy said. He hoisted Cling higher. And Cling saw his chance. His head struck like a snake's and his teeth fastened on Jimmy's wrist and bit in deep. Jimmy gave a yell of pain. His knife clattered at his feet. Halfmen burst from the forest and swarmed along the Leap. Some came at the gliders, some at Jimmy.

Jimmy tore his wrist free, leaving a strip of skin in Odo Cling's mouth. 'Get goin',' he yelled. Cling was working his own knife from its sheath. But Jimmy had him. He hefted him in the air, caught him by his leather shirt and the seat of his pants, took a step, and heaved him like a sack of oats off Sheercliff. Cling turned slowly in the air. He looked as if he had sprung from a trampoline. Then he began to fall, shrieking thinly. Down he went, down, arms and legs working. He grew smaller, smaller, until he was a dot, and still his shriek came winding up the cliff like a seabird's call. He splashed into the brown smoke and was gone.

'That's the end of 'im,' Jimmy said. He bent and picked up his knife. 'Now flap them wings, fer Pete's sake. I can 'andle this lot.'

The Halfmen were coming forward again. Jimmy charged to meet them. But they broke past him, heading for Susan.

'Go, fly Susan,' Breeze cried. She launched herself, fell, then her wings caught air and she sailed away. Brand followed her.

'Go on, Susan,' Nick cried. She was looking back at Jimmy, but Nick gave her a push that sent her off balance, and she took another step, looked down at the gleaming floor of smoke hundreds of metres below, and launched herself into the air. She flew from Deven's Leap.

11

Into the City

Susan wanted to turn back and see what had happened to Jimmy, but did not know how. She dared not shift her weight. Brand and Breeze were ahead and far below. She saw the wings of their gliders bright on the smoke, like paper fans. Nick must be behind her. She dared not turn her head. But soon she heard him yelling and he came up at her side, bouncing a little on the air. He waved at her. His glider swung away, then slid back closer. He looked close enough to touch.

'What happened to Jimmy?' she called.

'He's okay. At least, I think so. I circled back and had a look. They had him trapped, but they were scared of his knife. He really fixed Odo Cling.'

Susan did not want to think of that. And she could not agree that Jimmy was all right. Trapped by twenty Deathguards! Even his knife would not save him. But she had no time to worry. The glider was bumping about. She hung on tightly and concentrated on keeping still. Nick slipped a little below her.

'Come down a bit, Susan,' he yelled. 'I'm losing height. We've got to get down with Brand and Breeze or we'll get separated.'

'I can't come down.'

'Pull your weight forward a bit.'

'I can't.' She could see only his legs beneath the wings, but he swooped and laid his glider almost on its side, and climbed towards her. He could not make it all the way.

'Susan, do what I say. You've got to shift your weight. We're heavier than you and we're going down faster. You'll get left behind.' He fell away. Far below Breeze and Brand were almost in the smoke. And gradually Nick sank. He banked and climbed and fell again, and all the while his desperate calls grew thinner until at last they were no more than a squeak. Brand and Breeze vanished. The sun had sunk below the edge of the smoke. It was a deep-red ball burning up at her. The smoke seemed solid. She went down gradually towards it, towards the silver fan of sea glittering in its rim. Nick was fluttering like a moth far below.

'Susan, Susan,' came his call. Then he slipped into the smoke and she saw him no longer.

She felt that it was right she should be alone. He would find Brand and Breeze, he would be all right. There was no way they could help her. She had been alone since she had claimed the Halves. She felt a fearful happiness as she sped along above the smoke.

The fan of sea widened. She came over its point. Down there the Poison Water reached the ocean. It smeared the sea with grey. South was the City, and the Pit, under a lump of smoke like a swollen pudding. Far out over the water the sun, yellow again, sank its rim into the sea. She risked a tiny shift of weight. The glider turned gently. She was able to see Sheercliff, grey and gleaming, and the mountains, picked out by the sun. Soon she would have to turn again and dive into the smoke. But for a while she flew along its edge, sinking all the time. It towered in banks above her. She had seen stormclouds like this, fat and grey as pumpkins, too heavy for the sky, but they had never made her as frightened as this slowly turning greasy smoke. She felt if she went in she would choke and die.

'Ready, Susan,' she told herself. 'Right. Here goes.' But she did not go. It was not only fear held her back. Some intuition – perhaps even some memory that came from Freeman Wells, or from the Halves – advised her of a way less dangerous. So she kept on flying, dropping down the heaving flanks of smoke towards the sea. The wings of her glider drummed and vibrated. The sun went down and the clear western sky turned pink and yellow. The moon, that smaller moon with different markings, hanging low on the flank of smoke, enriched itself to the colour of cheese. She glimpsed it over her shoulder and risked turning for a better look.

Then she saw the island. It was far away, a thin crescent in the darkening sea. It stood clear of the shore by a kilometre or so, and to Susan it gave the hope of rest and safety, and a place to think what she must do. She leaned the glider into a slow curve and set off across the sea towards the island.

Soon she was flying in moonlight. The sea was silver and the island lay dark on it. She began to worry that it was too far away for her to reach. What was it Nick had said about shifting weight? She tried to push herself back a little – and it worked. The glider rose. But then it seemed to lose its speed and for a moment she thought it was going to fall out of the sky. There was a horrible lurch, and she was dropping. But the wings caught again, the air pressed up, and she was flying, the island was ahead, and she was safe. No more experiments! She was just going to hang there and let the glider fly, and hope she was going to make it.

The island came at her. She saw its cliffs in the moonlight, and saw banks of grass and patches of bush. But the sea was like a floor under her feet. She would be on it any moment. She headed for a beach, silver in a jaw of cliffs. And she risked one more shift, back a bit, a little to one side. The glider rose and banked, and she shifted again, the other way, and it swooped across the water, seagull fast, slanting at the beach. She did not quite get there. Her feet struck where the waves broke, and she ran a pace or two, sinking in. Then the glider tipped and she was sprawling on the sand in a tangle of harness and struts. Waves broke on her feet. She drew them up, and struggled with her straps, and freed herself. She ran up the sand and fell on her knees. Safe! She could hardly believe it.

In a moment she stood up and stumbled on. She was desperately tired. She knew she should explore the island. There were only a few moments of moonlight left. She should see if she was alone. But she had no strength. She came on to dry sand, and found some rocks still warm from the sun, and lay down close to them. She curled up. It had been cold flying, but now in her Woodland cloak and Halfman cloak, she was warm and safe. No food. No water. No way to get off the island. That was a worry for the morning. She smiled, and groaned contentedly, and went to sleep.

Morning came with a cold sea breeze. She was on the dark side of the island. She woke shivering, and rose stiffly to her feet. All her joints were aching. Her mouth was dry and she was hungry. Low cliffs stood behind her. In front the sea stretched unbroken to the horizon. The tide had come in during the night and floated her glider away.

She knew her first job was to find water. She climbed the rocks she had slept by and went across to the base of the cliffs looking for a pool. But of course, they were salt. Her only hope was to find a spring somewhere, or a rainwater pool. The island was too small to have a stream. She began to wish she had thought of that before landing.

The cliff sloped back easily and she climbed it through an elbow of bush and stood on the highest point of the island. It was really no more than a ridge standing up from the sea. The hollow of its crescent faced the horizon. There was the only beach – her beach. Reefs of black rock met the sea at every other point. Across the water the smoke stood up like a wall. It seemed less thick than she had thought. She caught hazy glimpses of a seashore and low buildings. They made her realize that people in the smoke could be watching her. She hurried along the island below the skyline and clambered down to the reef at the other end of the beach. And that was it – that was the island. No water. No food. She searched in the bush above the reef for some moss to suck, but found none. Perhaps she was going to die of thirst on this island. The thought struck her like the blow of a fist. She *had* to reach the Stone, she *had* to place the Halves. The trust was hers.

She searched the reef for driftwood. If she could make a raft she could float to the mainland. There was nothing. But as she searched she began to feel she was being watched. It came like a prickling on her spine. Several times she turned suddenly, but saw only cliffs, black rocks, the moving sea. Once she thought she heard a slither and splash. She ran to the spot, a cleft in the rocks with water heaving in it and brown ropes of kelp writhing about. She waited there. Nothing came. Apart from the sea, all was still.

For a while Susan sat on the beach, hugging her knees, thinking grimly. Water. Food. A way to get to land and to the City. There had to be an answer. She could not believe she was going to die here. There had to be someone who could help her. Then she thought of Breeze. What had she said? They would try to reach the coast, and ask for help from the Seafolk. Well, where would the Seafolk be if not in the sea – whoever they were? She could not believe she hadn't thought of it sooner. It came from pride, she thought, and from her belief that she was alone.

She ran back to the reef where she had heard the noise. She went to the cleft in the rocks and looked down at the kelp. She took a deep breath. 'Seafolk,' she called. 'Seafolk, I need your help.'

The water heaved. The kelp writhed. Nothing came.

'Seafolk. My name is Susan Ferris. I am not a Halfman though I wear a Halfman cloak. I have the Mark of Freeman Wells on my wrist. I have the Halves. I must reach the Mother-stone.'

Slap went the sea. The kelp made a salty rustling. Then a voice behind her croaked, 'Show me the Mark.'

She leapt around. Reclining there on flippers was a seal.

158

Water trickled on his fur. His cat-mouth smiled. His brown eyes watched with calm intelligence.

'Was that you? Were you talking?' Susan stammered.

'I do not like human speech. It gives me a pain in my throat. Show me the Mark.'

'Yes. Yes, of course,' Susan said. She bared her arm and walked up to the seal. 'I'm sorry about the dye. Breeze put it on to make us look like Halfmen.'

'Who is Breeze?'

'A Woodlander. She and Brand flew down from Sheercliff with me. And Nick. They came down in the smoke. I suppose you won't believe me if I tell you that I flew here?'

'I believe. I saw you land. Very clumsy. Flying should be left to birds. Yes, it is the Mark. Tell me your story.'

She trusted him – or her. She – yes, she – had a friendly face. It was more seal-like than human, but less seal-like than a seal's. She thought she saw human traces round the eyes and nose. Reddish fur, beautiful as satin, ran down to flippers like duck's feet, mottled many colours. They looked as if they might once have been human hands and feet.

'What's your name?'

'Island Lover. Do not make me use your ugly talk. It is like swallowing mussel shells. Tell me how you came here.'

Susan sat on a rock. She told her tale. Now and then Island Lover croaked. Her eyes were wonderfully expressive. They widened, sparkled, laughed, grew brown and heavy with sympathy. They watched Susan sharply as a hawk's and softly as a deer's.

'Indeed. Indeed. What an extraordinary tale.'

'It's true.'

'I believe you, child. We have heard of Freeman Wells. And we know Otis Claw. We see his smoke. It starts to poison our sea. And so you have the Halves?'

'Yes.'

'And you would go into the City?'

'Yes.'

'It will be dangerous.'

'I know.'

'It is your task. We will take you. Wait here. I will come back in the evening.' She turned and flipped with surprising speed towards the surging kelp.

'Island Lover,' Susan cried.

The seal stopped. 'Try not to make me speak. I feel as if I have a sea-egg stuck in my throat.'

'I'm sorry. But I'm thirsty. Can you tell me where I can find some water?'

'Water? Water? It is all about you.'

'Fresh water, I mean.'

'Ah, that tasteless stuff. Yes, you humans drink it. There is a spring at the other end of the island. High in the reef. The merest trickle. You can drink there.'

'And food? Is there any food?'

'Dig in the sand. There are shellfish. Feel under the ledges. There are oysters, mussels, sea-snails. This green weed in the pools is tasty. Do not touch the yellow. It is poisonous. Oh, my throat! Wait on the beach at sunset.' She undulated to the cleft and flipped into the kelp. Susan watched for her to come up, but nothing broke the water. Something red flashed below the surface further out.

It took Susan half an hour to find the spring. It filled a pool no bigger than a cup. She emptied it several times and waited impatiently for it to fill again. She collected mussels and oysters and broke them open with stones. They were fat and juicy. She tried eating them with the green seaweed, but found it too bitter. When she had eaten enough she went to the beach. It still lay in shadow, but the sun had reached the water. She took off her clothes, left the belt with the Halves where she could see it, and swam for an hour in the warm sea. The water had no effect on Breeze's dye. Then she sunbathed, trying to dream of home. But she found it impossible. The Halves kept intruding, she kept remembering what she must do. Later she climbed to the top of the island and lay in the grass, staring at the mainland. The smoke seemed thinner in the glare of midday. Once or twice she thought she saw Halfmen moving in it. She wondered where Nick and Breeze had come down, and if they were safe.

She ate and drank twice more before sunset. Then in the dusk she saw a boat approaching. It gave her a terrible fright. Halfmen must be coming. Seafolk would not need boats. She hid in the rocks by the spring and watched the boat glide swiftly on the purple sea. After a while she saw there was no one in it. It was no more than a hulk, with its deck-house pushed askew and holes rotted in its sides. In a moment she caught the red flash of a seal's head moving along the waterline. She came out from the rocks and ran down the beach. A seal reared up from the foam and splashed towards her.

'Are you Island Lover?'

'Surely you recognize your friends. Ah well, all humans look alike to me. We have brought a boat. We will take you up the river to the City. Hide in the cabin. Do not show yourself.'

The boat beached gently. Susan saw seals swimming about it, keeping it straight.

'Shall I get in now?'

'You will find food and water in the cabin. Yes, get in. The sun goes down. We will start. It is hard work, so don't rock the boat.'

Susan clambered in. The water foamed as the seals pushed the hulk out from the beach. She sat in the stern awhile, watching their shapes flashing in the water. Then the sun went down and dark came quickly. The island faded from sight. She went into the cabin. She could not see any danger, but felt it was only polite to obey Island Lover. The cabin was bare. A bottle and a pile of seaweed lay in a corner. She sat by them, feeling lonely.

The boat moved, slapping water. Now and then she felt a small shudder as the seals banged on its hull. After a while she lay down and slept on the grimy floor. The night went on, she dreamed it was growing darker and darker and darker. Black hands were pressing on her eyes, black hands were pouring some foul liquid down her throat. She woke choking, and at once smelled a carbide reek, and knew the boat had entered the smoke. She grabbed the hem of her cloak and covered her mouth and nose, and smelled at once the wonderful sweet scent of Shy. It flashed in colours through her. She felt her eyes grow clear and her heart beat strongly.

The motion of the boat was smooth – no slap of waves. She went outside and peered over the side. Far away, through the murk, lights shone dimly.

'Susan Ferris, is that you?' croaked a voice.

'Yes. Where are we?'

'In the river. Go back inside. We may meet other boats.'

'What time is it?'

'After midnight. We will be in the City by dawn.'

Susan went back inside. She drank some water. Then she lay down and tried to sleep again. But an urgent tattoo sounded on the boat. 'Susan.' She went back to the side. Island Lover's voice croaked softly, 'A dinghy comes. Go inside. Cover yourself with your cloak. Be still.'

She listened. From far off came the creak of oars. She peered but could not see anything.

'Go.'

She scuttled inside and lay in a corner and hid her face and hands under her cloak. Soon she heard voices calling. They had a metallic sound. Halfmen!

'There she is. Shine the light on her.'

A light played on the boat. It beamed dully through the deck-house window.

'She's a wreck. Not worth salvaging.'

'I'm going aboard. Might be something on her.'

Susan shrank deeper in her cloak. But the first voice said, 'Don't waste your time. There'll be better pickings along the shore.'

'Why was she drifting up river?'

'Tide was taking her up. It's turning now.'

The other man growled. ' Something fishy about this boat. She don't smell right.'

'She's been at sea so she stinks. Salt air. Filthy stuff.'

The dinghy bumped alongside and the light played through the deck-house door.

'Bah! An old bottle. A pile of stinkin' weed. Let's get going. I tell you mate, this thing's not worth the trouble. Full of holes. She'll be at the bottom of the river by morning.'

'Yeah,' growled the other, 'you're right. By Claw, I'd like to sink her with a few Goods on board.'

'There's no Goods left, mate. All had their throats cut. I cut a few myself. Let's go.'

The oars creaked. The dinghy splashed away. After a while Susan dared to breathe. It seemed she had smelt the stink of evil. She covered her mouth and nose and flooded herself with Shy. She felt a gentle touch on the boat. It began to move slowly on the thick water.

For the rest of the night she sat awake. Once or twice she peered out the windows, but saw no more lights and heard no alarms. The seals kept up their pressure, moving the boat heavily up-river against the tide.

When she guessed dawn was not far away, she drank the rest of the water from the bottle and chewed some seaweed. It still had a bitter taste, but she chewed and swallowed stolidly, telling herself she must keep up her strength. From occasional sounds, a clashing of iron, a shriek of pain, she guessed they were entering the City. She saw dim lights, the gleam of windows, gleam of muddy slipways, and saw the shapes of moored boats and long-legged jetties. The smoke drifted everywhere, like a mist.

Dawn came without colour. All that was black turned grey. The seals nosed the boat in under a jetty. Susan came out of the deck-house and looked over the side. Island Lover slid up close to her.

'Child, I beg of you, a mouthful of that weed.'

Susan ran back inside and brought out all the weed. Soon half a dozen seals had thrust up their heads and were chewing ecstatically.

'Delicious,' Island Lover croaked through her full mouth. She swallowed. 'This foul river poisons us. But now we will be strong enough to reach the sea. Susan, goodbye.'

'Where am I?'

'On the outskirts of the City. Soon it will wake. You must hide.'

'Yes. Thank you.' But knew she would not hide. She must find her way to the Pit, to the Motherstone.

'Climb up the ladder,' Island Lover said. 'We will push the boat out and let it drift away. May Ocean Spirit go with you.'

Susan climbed an iron ladder beside the boat. She stood shivering on the jetty. 'Goodbye,' she whispered. The seal heads vanished and the boat began to drift away on the Poison Water. She did not stay to watch it, but ran along the jetty and into a maze of tumble-down buildings. Here and there a light showed in a window. Once she saw a hooded shape moving sleepily. She kept close to the walls and hurried on, plunging deep into the City. She tried to think what Brand and Breeze had told her of it. Once it had been beautiful – parks and hanging gardens, a glass-clear river, shops and busy wharves and warehouses. Now everything stank. Buildings rotted by the broken streets. Foul gutters ran to the river, clogged with heaps of refuse. Stumps of trees stood like rotten teeth in the bare parks, where skinny dogs howled and moaned. The smoke lay over all, slow and brown and sticky. It lay pooled in corners, it stirred like dirty water, and floated after everything that moved.

Susan kept her cloak over her face. She hurried on, keeping close to walls, turning always into streets where the buildings were taller. Slowly the City woke. Halfmen came shuffling through the streets. She saw a man beating a chained dog. Its howls rose in a piteous wail. In a yard two men struggled over a scrap of food. Further on a woman was whipping a child. She was the first Halfwoman Susan had seen. Her hair came out of her hood in ragged wisps. She beat methodically, with the buckle end of a leather belt. The child rolled on the ground, screaming with a grey wide-open mouth. But as Susan watched, it wriggled under the blows and seized the woman's ankle in its teeth.

Susan ran and left them, the howling woman, the biting child, she ran on across gutters, under broken walls, through bare parks, and came to a square where Halfmen were clustered about a cart drawn by four chained half-naked men. A huge urn stood on it. A woman ladled food into basins thrust at her. It was a stew of the same greasy lumps Odo Cling had made Susan eat. Each Halfman turned with his food and gobbled privately. Then they snarled for more, jabbing with their elbows, thrusting up their basins. Men guarding the cart beat them away. They cracked their whips on the backs of the four in the shafts and the cart lumbered off.

Susan turned aside into a narrow street. Buildings leaned over it and a slimy gutter ran down the centre. But at the end, across another park of bare grey earth, she saw a coal-black building. It rose in tiers. That, she thought, must be Otis Claw's palace, built over the great hole called the Pit. That was where he held his daily court, and there, in the Pit, the Motherstone lay, safe in the dome of force Freeman Wells had built.

She hurried along the street. Half-way down she found the body of a man with his pockets turned out. He seemed to grin at her. She backed by him along the walls, and ran on, half sobbing. This place was a nightmare, this was Hell.

When she came out she saw the sun shining red in the smoke. It seemed tiny, far away. She could not believe it was the same yellow sun that burned over Wildwood. The black building rose tiered and ugly over the park. A few trees straggled there. Broken statues lay face down in the mud. Then she saw the building was as much factory as palace. This was where Otis Claw had his laboratories, and made the smoke that would cover the world, cover Wildwood, leak into the plains where the Birdfolk lived, and the underground world of Seeker and Watcher. It bubbled and seethed from a black chimney pointing like a gun-barrel at the sky.

Susan stood and watched it. She felt sick. But she had never been more angry. She breathed in Shy. She traced the shape of the Halves locked in her belt. Then she started across the park. Her feet slipped in the mud and the hem of her cloak trailed in filthy puddles. A starving dog snarled at her and then lay hopelessly down by a tree-stump. At the other side of the park she crossed a plank over a scummy ditch that had been a stream. She approached great barred gates where a crowd of a hundred Halfmen waited silently in the smoke. These, she guessed, were the early-comers for Otis Claw's court.

She stood as close to them as she dared. She did not want to make herself conspicuous by standing apart, but felt that if she moved among them one might look at her closely and see through her disguise. She stood still, and kept her head lowered, and held her hood about her face. The smell of Shy was delicate, comforting. She wondered if it would drift to the Halfmen close by. To them she supposed it would be a stink. She moved every now and then, keeping close to no one long. Voices murmured sourly, men snarled at each other. There was never any laughter. Once a man and a woman fought with knives. Guards rushed from the gates and dragged them away.

'More meat for the dogs,' said a Halfman.

'It'll spoil their appetite for the Woodland scum,' said another.

Susan reeled with shock. She almost fell. The Halfman gave her a push. 'Keep your hands to yourself. I'll slice you up.'

Woodland scum? She wanted to rush at the man, question him. Did it mean Brand and Breeze were captured? What had happened to Nick? And where were they? But she turned away, she shuffled off. She must not get caught. She must not. She had to get to the Motherstone. No one – Brand, Breeze, Nick – no one was safe unless she placed the Halves. Everyone would die.

She moved with lowered head down the edge of the crowd and leaned on a wall. Cautiously she looked back. A Halfman was watching her. He stood on the edge of the crowd, with his hood well forward and his fingers hooked in his belt. She could not see his face, but a gleam of eyes showed he was staring at her. She lowered her head. She tried to look casual. Her hands were trembling. In a moment she shifted slowly. She looked at him again, sideways. Yes, he was watching her. She tried to think what to do. He must suspect. If he came at her she would have to touch him with her wrist. But what would happen after that?

Another fight started in the crowd. People surged to watch, and the Halfman came striding at her, along their wall of backs. She thrust her arm at him, but he caught it in both hands and held it still. His white teeth grinned in his grey face.

'Thought it was you,' he whispered. 'Your eyes give you away. You better keep them shut.'

She put her head on his shoulder. She felt tears on her face. Under the roars of blood-lust and the shriek of someone stabbed, she whispered, 'Nick, oh Nick. Thank God. I thought they must have caught you. I thought you must be dead.'

12

Motherstone

He hurried her down the side of the square. They found a boarded-up doorway in a crooked street.

'I've been waiting since dawn,' Nick said. 'I knew if you hadn't been caught this is where you'd come.'

'Nick, they've captured Brand and Breeze. I heard a man talking about feeding them to the dogs.'

'They'd bring them here first to see Otis Claw. What we've got to do is get into the Pit. Maybe we can save them. Have you still got the Halves?'

'Yes.' She told him about the island and the Seafolk.

'You flew better than me,' he said. 'There was almost no lift in the smoke. I came down in a swamp. I never saw Brand and Breeze.' But, hiding that night in the fringes of the swamp, he had heard hounds barking and men shouting. He had thought they were hunting him. But they went by as he huddled in the reeds and he knew they must be on another trail.

'Brand and Breeze?'

'Yes. Anyway, I set out for the City. I knew I had to find you. I got here last night and slept in a ruined building. There were huge rats. Ugh!'

'Have you had anything to eat?'

'No. I can get by. I drank some water. Pretty smelly stuff. We'd better get back, Susan. I think they're getting ready to open the gates.'

They went to the square, keeping their heads low and hoods pulled forward, and stood at the back of the crowd. Soon they were hemmed in. The gates rumbled open and a surge of Halfmen carried them through. They shuffled along in a grey darkness, down an endless ramp, deeper and deeper into the bedrock under Otis Claw's palace. The reek of sweat, the press of elbows, knees, torsos, the heat of massed bodies, the ugly snarling, overpowered them. But they kept a secret clasp of hands, kept their Shy as close as they dared to their faces. Guards posted at intervals down the ramp jabbed the crowd with spear butts, forcing it on.

The ramp curved in a slowly tightening circle. Nick guessed they must be half a kilometre underground. It was like being in a giant beehive, buried in earth. The busyness was there, the ceaseless humming, and guards darting angrily, like soldier bees. But here instead of honey, poison was made; and at the centre, in the Pit, they would find no queen, but Otis Claw.

At last the stone floor levelled out, the press eased, and Nick and Susan moved more freely. They let go hands. No Halfman would show affection. They went through another set of iron gates, a set of huge stone doors, and climbed a ramp into the chamber known as the Pit. It was vast and shadowy. The walls and ceiling showed dimly in the lamplight. In a basin-like depression in the floor lay the dome of force. It resembled a great glowing apple. Its light did not shine out, but kept to itself. It was soft, inviolate, standing high above the Halfman guards. Set in it was the Motherstone – grey, prosaic, sitting like an office desk on the floor. The guards were just as Marna had said: two rows, shoulder to shoulder, one facing the Stone, the other facing out. Susan saw at once there was no way through. She turned and looked at Otis Claw.

He sat on a throne of obsidian. She had never seen anyone more ugly. Marna had described him as a handsome youth, a golden youth. Twenty years of power and gratified lust had made him foul. He lolled on his throne in great folds of flesh. A bony skull was at the top of him, and all his flesh seemed to have fallen away from that grey point, into monstrous cheeks, and serried jowls melting on his breast, and a belly sagging sack-like, and thighs that quivered in their black silk casings. His eyes were, strangely, merry. They were little black marbles. They twinkled with a dark and secret glee. With his ruined hand, his claw, the Paingiver, Otis Claw, toyed with a broken chain about his neck.

Susan and Nick had let the crowd push past them. They stood at the back, close to the wall by the ramp. They heard the doors grind shut. Across one flank of the basin Otis Claw sat on his throne. They had a clear view, and saw at his back Halfmen holding five black dogs on leashes. A man in leather stepped forward from the throne-side: a small man, sharp and evil. For a moment Susan thought he was Odo Cling come back to life. But no, he was the new Cling, Cling's replacement. There would be no shortage.

'Kneel to the Lord Darksoul,' he cried. 'Kneel to the Paingiver.'

At once the crowd was on its knees. The guards were on their knees. Only those about the Motherstone did not move. Nick and Susan were slow, but got down before anyone saw them.

'Lick the dust,' cried the man.

The crowd licked. Susan and Nick, with shrinking tongues, pretended.

A new voice came, a voice both dead and jolly. Otis Claw. 'Good, good, well done my slaves. Rise up. We shall hear your troubles. We shall see which among you shall be rewarded – and which shall feed my dogs. Although today they will taste other meat.'

The crowd rose to its feet, humming with anticipation.

'Let me hear the first case,' Otis Claw said. Up at the front someone stepped forward. The sound of disputing voices rose and fell.

Susan looked about the hall again. Down by the Motherstone the guards stood shoulder to shoulder. She wondered if Nick could set up some disturbance, draw them away. But no – looking at them she knew they would never move. Was there some way she could jump over the top, jump into the dome of light and reach the Stone? She remembered what Marna had said – the dome of force would recognize the wearer of the Mark and welcome her – or was it receive her? Yes, receive her. And suddenly she had it, and she almost gave a shout. She put her hand on her cloak and felt the small soft lump of the stone-silk gloves in the pocket of her shorts. She looked at the walls of the Pit, looked at the ceiling. Seeker had known.

'Nick,' she breathed. He leaned close to her. 'When something happens up there move back slowly with me into that opening.'

He gave a small nod of understanding. They waited. Cries of anger rose, then yells of pleading. Someone was being set to run against the dogs. They did not watch, but heard the crowd roar, and heard the dogs snarling, yelping, tearing.

'Do not let them eat,' Claw cried. 'Ha! he ran well.'

Nick and Susan backed cautiously down the wall. They came to a gap between two buttresses of stone and slipped back into shadow.

'Nick, I'm going to climb. Remember what Marna said, the light would receive me?'

'Yes, but –'

'I'm going to get over it and drop.'

'Susan –'

'Can you think of any other way?'

He could not. 'They'll see you.'

'I'll go up in the shadow between these ribs of stone. Once I'm on the ceiling I'll just have to hope they don't look up.'

Otis Claw's thick laughter rang in the hall. A man screamed.

'Good luck,' Nick whispered. 'I'll get back in the crowd. I might be able to make some sort of fuss to stop them looking.'

She lifted her cloaks and drew out the stone-silk gloves. But before she could pull them on the doors of the Pit ground heavily open. The crowd gave a bark of anticipation. Brand and Breeze came stumbling up the ramp, roped together, prodded on by Halfman spears. Their black cloaks were gone, they were in Wildwood green, but green torn and filthy with swamp mud and stained with blood.

'Nick –'

'Go on. Up. It's our only chance to save them.'

The guards about Brand and Breeze opened a path through the crowd. But Halfmen poked with their knives, gnashed their teeth, spat and snarled. The guards beat them back and brought the prisoners in front of Otis Claw's throne. In the shadows, Susan drew on her stone-silk gloves. They clasped her hands and arms in a friendly way. She drew the stockings on her feet.

'Get back into the crowd, Nick.'

He gave her shoulder a pat, and was gone. She could not tell which black hood was his in that sea of hoods. She reached out her hands. Eagerly the stone-silk met the stone. Even through her double thickness of cloaks it fixed itself with a steely strength. Susan began to climb.

In the crowd Nick wriggled by straining Halfman bodies. He dug with his elbows, and was gone before hands could fix on him. He heard cries from the front of the crowd, and heard the dogs baying eagerly. When he got to the front he dropped to his knees and peered through a gap in the line of guards holding back the crowd from Otis Claw's throne. The dogs, huge, black, muscular, red-mouthed, were straining at Brand and Breeze, but their handlers held them back. The crowd was screaming for blood. Otis Claw made a sign to his officer. The man stepped forward and cried in a voice thin and deadly as a knife, 'Silence!' At once the hall was deathly still. Even the dogs made no sound. The only noise Nick heard was the rasp of the Woodlanders' breathing. They held each other and looked as if they were about to collapse.

'Kneel before Darksoul,' the officer cried.

Brand and Breeze swayed, they almost fell. But Brand said, 'Woodlanders kneel to no man.' At once guards ran forward and beat them with their spear butts to their knees.

Otis Claw smiled. 'Now,' he said kindly, 'let me hear your tale. Then I must feed my dogs. The poor creatures are hungry.'

'Ha-a,' laughed the crowd.

'Tell me how you flew down from Sheercliff. And tell me of the death of my servant, Odo Cling.'

'We will not speak to you,' Breeze said.

Claw smiled again. 'Oh, you will speak. I have ways of seeing to that. But let us do things pleasantly. Where is the Mixie girl who holds my Halves? My pretty ornaments? How can I fix my chain until I have them? I may let you go if you give me her.'

'We will not speak.'

'Does she mean to bring them here and place them on the Stone? Look, Woodlanders. Do you really think she could find a way through my guards?'

Even Nick looked into the hollow where the guards stood two-deep, immovable as stone.

'She will find a way,' Breeze said.

'Ha!' Claw laughed. 'A girl! A Mixie girl! She will enter my hall? She will find a way through my guards? This amuses me.'

'She will find a way.'

'And the boy? The Mixie boy? Where is he? My guards have found his flying machine. They scour the countryside for him. Tell me where he is.'

'We do not know.'

'Look at my dogs. They are hungry.'

'We flew first. We did not see Nick or Susan again.'

'Nor will you ever. I grow tired of this. Let us have some sport.' He nodded at the dog handlers. But before they could move, an old grey dog Nick had not noticed before stood

173

up from beside Claw's throne and began to growl. He was ancient, he tottered on his legs, but Nick felt his hair begin to prickle. The dog had his wet eyes fixed on him.

Claw reached down and grasped the animal by its collar. For the first time he looked alert. His little eyes gleamed. 'Hold. Something troubles Gnasher.'

'Lord,' the officer said, 'he was trained to sniff out mixed men.'

'I know that, fool! So, there is a Mixie in my hall. Ha, ha! Good. They come to me.'

Nick got to his feet. He had thought he was brave but those terrible dogs were more than he could face. Yet he did not run. Delay – delay was everything. He must buy time for Susan while she climbed. He risked a look behind, over the crowd. The shadow where Susan was climbing reached up in a long inverted V. He could not see her. She was still in there. But when she came to the ceiling, when she was in the open, it was up to him to see that no one looked.

Claw raised his voice. 'Listen,' he cried, 'listen slaves. There is a Mixie in my hall. Every man must turn back his hood. I must see every face. Obey me now or I shall tell my guards to kill you all.'

At once the Halfmen obeyed. They reached up, turned their black hoods back, and their grey heads gleamed dully in the light. Eagerly, each man turned to his neighbour. Nick was the only person who had not moved. At once a dozen pair of hands tore at him, hands tore back his hood and showed his hair.

'Do not kill him,' Claw cried, 'bring him to me.'

Guards rushed into the crowd and dragged him free. They pushed him into the open beside Brand and Breeze. He stood there shaking, trying to look defiant.

'Kneel,' cried the officer. 'Kneel to the Lord Darksoul.'

'No –' A spear butt struck him between his shoulders and knocked him down.

Claw smiled. He had small sharp teeth and glistening gums. 'See how easy it is. Tell me who you are.'

Nick caught his breath. 'My name is Nicholas Quinn,' he managed to say.

'Nicholas Quinn. And you are the Mixie boy? Where is the girl?'

'She's dead,' Nick said.

'Oh Nick. Oh, no,' cried Breeze.

'I'm sorry. She – she couldn't control her glider. It went out over the sea. She must be drowned.' He hated lying to Breeze. Her face was crumpled with grief. Brand too had slumped. They had no hope. But he had steered Otis Claw away from Susan. He saw his face smiling benevolently.

'Drowned? Oh, how sad. We must set up a memorial statue to her. A bird perhaps, like the Birdmen of Morninghall, who soon will be my subjects. A pity, boy, that you will not live to see it. But my dogs are hungry. Their diet is monotonous. You will make a change.'

'I can show you how to make gliders,' Nick said.

'Ha,' Claw said, 'I do not need toys. I have men and they have knives. And I have my smoke.'

'I can tell you where to find Jimmy Jaspers. He's the one who killed Odo Cling.' He heard Brand and Breeze gasp and felt them shrink away. He did not look at them. Anything, anything to keep Otis Claw talking, to keep him from looking up. Susan must be on the ceiling by now.

'Jimmy Jaspers?' Claw said. 'I have heard of him. He was my agent. I have reserved a special death for him. But I do not need Mixie boys to tell me how to find him. I will find him. And before he dies I will thank him for ridding me of Cling. Cling wished to sit on my throne. My throne! The throne of the Paingiver! Ha! But enough of this. Hear how my poor dogs whimper. Which of you will run first?'

'I can tell you a secret pass to Morninghall. I can tell you where the Woodland villages are. I can –'

175

'Silence.' The spear butt struck Nick again, knocking him on his face. Claw looked down at him narrowly. 'This boy keeps me talking. Why is that?'

'Lord, perhaps the girl is not dead. Perhaps she is in the hall.'

'No,' Nick said, and the spear butt struck him again. He blacked out for a moment, and when he came to he saw the old grey dog on its feet, pointing its nose at the ceiling, and in the silent hall, heard it give a single hungry yelp before it collapsed. Claw looked up. Nick looked up. Half-way between the top of the wall and the ceiling's centre Susan clung to the stone, spread out like a moth.

Otis Claw screamed. It was a cry both of rage and pain. He rose from his throne. His belly trembled and his huge thighs quaked.

'Who is that? Who is that who crawls upon the stone?' His voice went winding up into the gloom towards that black moth-shape like the fearful cry of a lost child. No answer came. The watchers saw an arm move, and then a second arm, and the shape inched forward.

'Who? Who is it?' He sent his cry at Nick and the Wood-landers. His sagging face had a look of desperate woe, and his little dome of skull, bare as a tennis ball without its fur, bobbed in a panic.

Breeze answered, 'It is Susan Ferris.'

'She has the Halves?'

'She has them, Otis Claw. Your time is done.'

'No, no,' he screamed. 'I am Lord! I! Guards. Throw your spears. The one who brings her down shall share all the treasures of the land. He shall rule Wildwood in my name. Throw! Spear her!'

The guards about the Stone left their posts. They ran to the lip of the basin, set themselves, and hurled their spears up into the gloom at Susan crawling slowly across the stone. The spears fell short. The ceiling was too high. The guards ran and retrieved them, threw again. Those from the walls, those about the throne, ran to join them. In the crowd people screamed as the spears rained down. Others were throwing knives wildly at Susan. The air was thick with weapons. But Susan was well clear. Though her weight pulled her in a painful arc she kept on, one arm after the other. To Nick she seemed to slide forward like a snail.

He and Brand and Breeze had slipped back to the wall beyond the throne. The old dog tottered at them with bared teeth, then lay and panted. Farther off, the hounds bayed at Susan. Nick picked up a knife and cut Brand and Breeze free.

'Nick, how can we help her?'

'She's all right. They can't throw their spears that far.'

'What is she going to do?'

'Fall into the light.'

'Ah, yes. The light will receive her. Marna said.'

Otis Claw ran wobbling down to the edge of the basin. He stood there, a great jelly-figure in black silk. 'Hold! Hold your spears. Fetch bowmen. Quickly. Arrows will bring her down.'

Guards ran out of the hall.

'You cannot get away, Mixie. We will pin you like a beetle.'

The crowd roared. But Susan moved forward. Her cloak flapped beneath her. Her hood had fallen back and her yellow hair streamed down.

'She's nearly there,' Nick said.

Three Halfmen ran through the crowd, holding great black bows. They stood on the edge of the basin.

'Shoot her down,' Otis Claw cried.

The first man set his arrow on the cord. Nick darted out from behind the throne. He ran across the open space and clawed on to the man's back. They rolled down into the basin. The arrow sped off at a tangent over the Motherstone. The second man had his arrow set. Brand seized the knife. He threw it and it lodged in the man's thigh. He gave a scream and dropped his bow. Breeze sped towards the third man. She was too late. He had his arrow notched. He drew it back, released it, and it sped in a black flash into the gloom, into the very apex of the ceiling, where Susan lay spread-eagled on the stone.

Only Brand and Breeze with their Woodland eyes saw what happened next. To the Halfmen, even to Nick, the arrow seemed to pierce her. But Brand and Breeze saw her release her hold an instant before the arrow struck. It pierced her cloak and lay across her throat. Claw gave a yelp of triumph. The Halfmen squealed and capered. And Susan fell.

Later she told Nick she had had no fear. It was as if a hand was waiting to catch her. She turned as she fell. Her black cloak trailed like a broken wing. She fell head first, and turned slowly over and stretched out her arms. It was as if she was reaching out to embrace someone. The great dome of light looked like a pool. She fell towards it, she came down like a stone, but to her it was like floating. She saw Nick's face, horrified, wailing up at her, and told him later that she smiled at him.

The light received her. She came down on the curve of one side but it drew her in, and slowed and settled her, and turned her slowly, easily, on to her feet. It was like floating in honey. Warm and sweet, it lapped her round. She opened her mouth and drank it in, and held her eyes wide and let it wash them. Everything outside was golden. Even Otis Claw and the Halfmen were golden. She saw them on the basin slopes, and saw Claw on the rim, his face collapsing into rage and grief. She saw Nick only a step away, and spoke to him. Then she turned and looked at the Motherstone. It was grey, ordinary, a simple slab, but it did not disappoint her. She sensed the huge powers sleeping in it.

She took off her Halfman cloak and dropped it with its piercing arrow beside her. She stood in Woodland green, and smiled at Brand and Breeze, coming to stand with Nick. Then Otis Claw was there, in front of them.

'Girl, Mixie,' he cried. His voice was raging, pleading, it wobbled uncontrolled between the two. 'Girl, do not, I order you, I Otis Claw order you. I am Darksoul, I am Paingiver. You cannot disobey me.'

She looked sadly at him. She unbuckled her belt from under her cloak and took out the Halves. She held one in each hand. Otis Claw saw them. His eyes bulged.

'I will give you half my kingdom. You shall rule with me. You shall have riches, slaves.'

Susan shook her head.

'Give them to me. I beg you. They are *mine*.'

She bared her arm. She placed the good Half first, then the bad. They lay on her wrist a moment like ornaments. Then they started to glow. The good Half glowed blindingly in gold, the bad in a red that was almost black. Their radiance dulled the light of Freeman Wells's dome and filled the Pit. And Susan seemed to shrink and she grew pale. She sank to her knees. Then the Halves faded a little, they settled into a steady light, one warm, one cold. She picked them off her wrist and rose to her feet. Again she smiled sadly at Otis Claw. She approached the Motherstone.

Claw had no cry left. He made broken mouthings. He jabbered with rage and terror. With hand and claw he attacked the dome. He raked at it, trying to come at Susan.

White light gave a single flash on the curve, printing him there, flesh and arteries, skeleton and organs. A clap like thunder sounded in the Pit. Otis Claw fell back, charred and dead. All about, Halfmen whined and shrieked. They ran about like ants in a broken nest. Nick and Brand and Breeze huddled together. They sheltered each other, and watched Susan in the light approach the Motherstone and reach out the Halves, one in each hand, and fit them in their places. A tiny thread of light ran round them in a circle, through them in an S, fusing them in the Stone and to each other. That was all. The Motherstone made no sign.

But outside, every Halfman fell on the ground. All over the Pit they groaned and thrashed. They beat their heels on the stone floor, they pounded with their fists, their faces snarled and writhed. They rolled over. Some drew themselves tightly into balls. The bowmen, the guards, the dog-handlers, the officer, all fell to the ground. The officer shrieked. He seemed in special pain. The dogs fled, howling.

'What's happening?' Nick said.

Susan stepped from the light. She was pale and weary. She gave a small scared smile. 'The good and bad are coming back in Balance.'

They huddled together, clinging with tight hands.

'Each had the seed in him,' Breeze said, 'and now it grows.'

'It takes them like an illness,' Brand said.

'Can we help them?'

'No. We must let them be. It may be days before they are well. Look about. Already they are going into coma.'

'What will they be like when they wake up?'

'They will be in Balance. They will be what they should be. Probably more bad than good, that is the way with men. But good will have its chance. They will choose.'

'Is it like this everywhere?'

'Wherever there are Halfmen in the world.'

With whimpers of pain, with little murmurs that might have been of pleasure or of fright, the Halfmen were drowning into sleep. Their convulsions had left them stained with sweat and scratched by their own fingernails. Now they sank. Their whimpers died. A cold silence settled on the Pit. Even the body of Otis Claw seemed to sleep.

'The Halves are on the Stone,' Breeze said. 'Who knows what will come of it? Now we must go back to our own land.'

They made their way out of the Pit, up into the City, into Manhome.

13

An Exchange of Gifts

They walked two days through Otis Claw's ruined land, and came to Sheercliff. Breeze had recovered her food-pack from the guards. They ate dried fern roots and boiled their water from streams, and kept their pads of Shy over their faces. Everywhere they passed Halfmen and Halfwomen, children too, lying as though dead. Breeze could not say how long it would be before they woke.

Climbing the path on Sheercliff, they met men coming down – Mixed men now, whole men. Some smiled, some were hostile, others merely looked dazed. A natural colour had come back to their skins.

'We have been slaves too long,' one man said.

'Otis Claw is dead,' Brand replied, 'the Halves are on the Stone.'

'We must stop his filthy smoke, we must bring our land to life.' He went on down.

Nick and Susan, Brand and Breeze, climbed out of the smoke into the sunshine. They breathed freely at last. The children threw away their Halfman cloaks. Verna and Dale and Jimmy Jaspers were waiting at the top of the path.

'Jimmy, you got away,' Susan cried.

'Yup,' Jimmy said, 'they didn' 'ave no leader without Cling. They started scrappin' among themselves. So I charged 'em an' they run away squawkin' like chooks.'

'What's wrong with your arm?'

'Cling 'ad a poison bite. It got swole up. Verna give me some medicine. I'm all right now.'

They found a stream and washed the filth of Darkland from their bodies. They scrubbed off the dye with sand. Susan and

Nick put on the sneakers Verna had fetched from Deven's Leap.

'What will happen in Darkland?' Susan asked.

'The wind will drive the smoke away, the rivers and sea will dissolve it. One day the land will be green again. What men will make of it, who can say?'

They travelled through Wildwood to Shady Home. Susan rested there. She was very tired. She felt as if she were recovering from a long illness. She lay in the sun, Breeze brought her fruit and berry juice, and Jimmy Jaspers, pieces of baked trout. She grew strong again. At night the Woodlanders sat about their fires and sang new songs – about Susan and Nick and Jimmy and the placing of the Halves. Nick began to talk about making a new glider.

'No, Nick. We've got to go.'

'Back home, you mean? – I suppose you're right.'

'I love this world. I love O. But we can't live here.'

Next day they started for the mineshaft. Five of them: Nick and Susan and Jimmy, with Brand and Breeze as guides. Verna wept as she said goodbye. They travelled north through Wildwood and followed the Sweet Water east towards the mountains. One day they came to a place Susan knew.

'This is where you rescued me from Odo Cling.'

It was all familiar after that. They went up step by step over the plateaux. They went through the gorge where Susan had tried to escape. She shivered at the memory of the Death-guard falling, and touched her birthmark. Now it was just a mark, no life in it. She was glad though that it had not faded away.

Up they went, ledge after ledge, Brand leading, Nick whistling tunes. He was happy and eager, getting ready for home. Jimmy Jaspers was quiet. And Susan grew sad. There were many things she was going to miss about O. She was even going to miss the danger.

Early one afternoon they climbed on to the tongue of rock

in front of the cave. Jimmy snarled at some memory. He scratched his chest. But the cave was neither threatening nor inviting, it simply stood there, a black opening into another world – their own. They did not look at it. They sat on the sun-warmed rock and ate their last meal with Brand and Breeze.

Then Nick and Susan stood up and took off their Woodland cloaks. They stood in their T-shirts and shorts.

'Well . . .' Susan said.

'Are you ready, Jimmy?'

'I been thinkin' as we come along,' Jimmy said.

'What Jimmy?'

'I'm gunner stay 'ere. If they'll 'ave me.' He looked at Brand and Breeze. 'I know it's not my world.'

'We will have you, Jimmy Jaspers.'

'But Jimmy –'

'I got no one back there. An' the fact is, the cops want to talk to me. But look, girl, look.' He swept his arm out, and they looked: the curving mountains, the blue south, Wildwood and the sea. And north: unknown lands.

'There's country out there, girl. Mountains, rivers. First orf, I'm gunner build that bridge I bust. Then I'm goin' explorin'. Reckon I'll see how big this Wildwood is. An' I'll go and visit them Pretty Pollies again and 'ave a look at them mountains over the plains. I might even get as far as them 'ot-lands I've 'eard about, where them pussycats live. An' then when I gets too old I'll sit down by one of these rivers an' pan me some gold.'

'You won't be able to spend it, Jimmy.'

'It's lookin' fer it that counts, not spendin' it. I know that now.'

'Jimmy, here. I want you to have this.' She took the Birdfolk feather from her neck. It flashed in the midday sun, blue and red. She put it in his hands.

'Girl – girl – I done some bad things to yer.'

183

'Keep it, Jimmy. Wear it for me.'

'I will. I will, Susie. I'll name a mountain after yer.'

'I'd rather have a waterfall. Nick can have a mountain.'

'OK. It's a deal.' He put the feather round his neck.

Susan turned to Brand. She felt in her pocket and drew out the stone-silk gloves. 'These belong in O. I want you to have them, Brand.'

'Thank you, Susan. They will stay in Shady Home. They will be our treasure. And I will go to the Great Throat and tell the Stonefolk what you have done.'

Susan smiled. She sighed. 'Breeze –' she unbuckled her belt '– this is for you. The belt Redwing made. You can keep your medicine in it where I kept the Halves.' She helped Breeze buckle it on. 'Now we've got nothing but what we came with.'

'You have some time outside your time,' Brand said. 'And you have memories. You take something back.'

'And this as well,' Breeze said. 'I have something for you.' She held out a tiny box carved from wood. It was no bigger than a walnut shell. 'Look in it, Susan. You will find something there beyond all price.'

Susan took the box. Carefully she opened it. Green silk made a lining, and on that lay a tiny dot of brown, a paper-flake. Although she had never seen one, she knew what it was.

'A seed, Breeze? A seed?'

'A seed of the Shy. Find a secret place in your world. A place where no one will come. Plant it there. The Shy will grow if you plant with love. One day it will flower. Then, if you wish, you can come back and visit us.'

'Oh thank you, Breeze. Thank you.'

'If you come, bring Nick with you. The Shy is his as well.'

Susan closed the box. She put it in her pocket. She and Breeze hugged each other. Then Breeze felt in her cloak and drew out two small flowers, one for each, the Shy whose scent would carry them back to Earth. Nick and Susan took them carefully.

'You know what to do?'

'We know.'

'Then goodbye, Susan Ferris. Goodbye, Nicholas Quinn.'

'I wouldn' mind comin',' Jimmy said. 'I could do with a feed of boiled mutton an' spuds.'

'Goodbye.'

Nick and Susan walked into the cave. They looked back once. Brand and Breeze and Jimmy stood against a backdrop of Wildwood. Nick waved. Susan gave a tiny smile. She could not tell whether it was happy or sad. Then they went on. It grew dark. They felt their way forward, hand in hand.

'What time shall we choose?'

'How about lunch? Midday?'

'All right. Twelve o'clock. We'll only have been gone for a couple of hours.' They laughed nervously.

Soon they came to the end of the tunnel.

'I can't see a thing.'

'Nor me. Let's go quickly, Nick. I don't like it here.'

'Right. Midday, remember. Are you ready?'

'Yes.'

They raised the Shy to their faces, drew their breath in deeply, and that magical perfume flooded them. It was so sweet that all the pain of going back, all the pain of sinking, whirling, drowning, touched them no more sharply than a feather. They saw each other printed on the dark, saw each other sink, they lost their hold on each other's hands, but rose again from that flooding dark, and found themselves hand in hand once more, kneeling in cold water, in a world they knew was theirs.

'Nick, Nick, we're through.'

'Yes, we're home.'

They stood up. The Shy flowers were gone from their hands. Through dripping water, past rotten props, in dark, in a grey light, they ran out of the mineshaft, they burst out into the midday sun. For a moment it blinded them. Then they saw everything, blue sky, white clouds, the weed-grown tailing mounds, Lodestone Creek, trees, creepers, a fantail darting in the trunks. They heard it cheep.

'Oh Nick, I'm glad we're back.'

'Look,' Nick said. Jimmy Jaspers' pack lay on the stones. Beside it was a tiny blue bottle. Nick picked it up. He could not find the cork. He pushed it down among Jimmy's shirts and trousers. Then he dragged the pack into the shaft and left it.

'Come on. Let's go home.'

They climbed above the gorge, went through the bush, crossed the paddock. Susan felt the little box with the Shy seed in her pocket. Tomorrow she would find a place and plant it. Only Nick would know. She did not believe she would ever go back to Wildwood, back to O, but it would be nice to have Shy growing in her world. She stroked her birthmark.

They went on to the swing bridge. Suddenly Nick started laughing. He pointed at his sneakers. 'They were brand new. Now they're worn to tatters. What am I going to tell Mum?'

'Mine too.'

'And look at your hair. It's grown two inches longer all in one morning.'

'Oh Nick, what will we tell them?'

They went on hand in hand.

'I'll think of something,' Nick said.